W9-CAF-481

1 *Born in Oxford, Massachusetts, December 25, 1821*

2 *Begins her first day as a schoolteacher, 1836*

3 *Receives a pass through the lines to distribute supplies and nurse wounded Civil War soldiers, 1862*

4 *Establishes an office to locate soldiers missing in action, 1865*

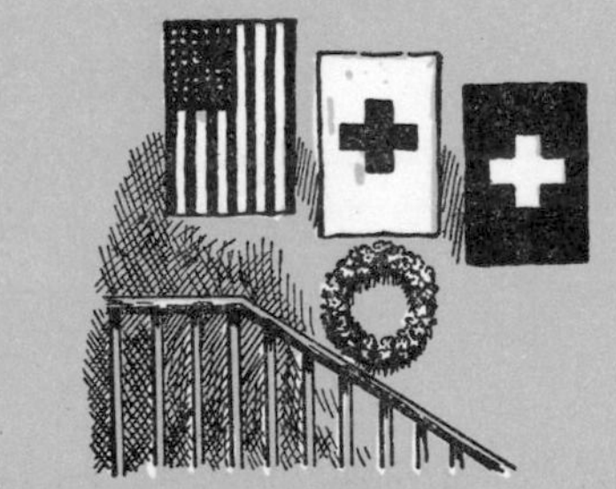

10 *Dies at Glen Echo, Maryland, April 12, 1912*

9 *Works to relieve suffering caused by the hurricane at Galveston, Texas, 1900*

GREAT EVENTS
IN THE LIFE OF
CLARA BARTON
6
Supervises the distribution
of relief to the poor
in Strasbourg, Germany, 1871
Helps organize military hospitals
during the Franco-Prussian War, 1870
8
Brings Red Cross aid to the victims of the
Johnstown, Pa., flood, 1889
7
Becomes the first president
of the American Red Cross, 1881

THE STORY OF

Clara Barton

The soldiers now welcomed Clara everywhere

THE STORY OF Clara Barton

By OLIVE PRICE

Illustrated by RUTH IVES

ENID LAMONTE MEADOWCROFT
Supervising Editor

PUBLISHERS Grosset & Dunlap NEW YORK

PRINTED IN THE UNITED STATES OF AMERICA

Library of Congress Catalog Card No. 54–5857

For My Friend

Elsie Singmaster Lewars

who has written many fine books

for children and so well served

the Red Cross

Contents

Illustrations

THE STORY OF
Clara Barton

"I have boys and girls to play with now"

CHAPTER ONE

Over the Hills and Far Away

THE chattering of blue jays awakened eight-year-old Clara. The birds were swinging on the vines that twined around her window. For a drowsy moment Clara thought she was back in her old home across the fields, where she had been born.

"But I'm not there at all!" she thought, sitting up in bed. "I'm in our new house in North Oxford and it's such fun to be here! I have girls and boys to play with now!"

She was glad her father had bought this big Massachusetts farmhouse. It had belonged to the Widow Learned, who had five children. Clara's father had told Mrs. Learned that she might live in a separate wing of the house until her children were grown up.

Mr. Barton had also given a home to an orphan boy named Lovett Stimpson. Since three of the Learned children were boys, Lovett lived in their wing of the house. And now, for the first time in her life, Clara had companions near her own age.

"And how I will miss them today!" she thought, as she jumped out of bed. "I wish they hadn't all gone to visit the Learned cousins in Boston!"

As she began to dress, Clara wiggled her nose in delight. The smell of good things to eat was all through the house! She brushed her hair and raced down to the kitchen.

"Oh, Mother!" she cried, "something smells wonderful!"

Mrs. Barton was peeking into the oven.

"I'm doing the Friday baking," she said, looking up with a smile. "I thought I'd get at it early." She cleared a space on the kitchen table. "Now you sit here and eat your breakfast."

Clara put on a little blue apron. It matched the ribbon on her hair and added a gay splash of color to her yellow dress. Her brown eyes danced as she looked at the table.

"You must have been up with the sun," she said, "to have a chocolate cake and all these pies baked so soon!"

"Yes, I was up with the sun," Mrs. Barton replied. "I saw your sisters off to school. They

both had to leave early, because they are giving examinations to their history classes this morning."

Clara smiled as her mother picked up a jug of maple syrup and put it near her plate.

"I'm glad Sally and Dorothy are teachers,"

she said. "It's nice that they can give me lessons at home when I don't go to school!"

As Clara began to eat her breakfast, she thought how lucky she was to have two sisters like Dorothy and Sally, and two brothers like Stephen and David. Some people said that they spoiled her because she was so much younger than they. Clara didn't think she was spoiled, of course!

She wished Stephen and David lived with them here. But they had stayed in the old homestead because it was closer to David's business at the Barton sawmill.

Glancing out of the window, Clara thought suddenly what fun it would be to go riding today. David had taught her to ride when she was only five years old. Now she was as much at home in a saddle as she was in her mother's rocking chair.

This was not strange, because Clara's father raised thoroughbred horses. Morgan colts and Highlander yearlings roamed in the pasture behind the house. Whenever Clara went into the pasture they followed her around, hoping she had brought them lumps of sugar.

"I must remember to take them some sugar

today," Clara thought. Then she spoke to her mother again. "Where is Father?" she asked.

"David and Stephen came over early to get him," said Mrs. Barton as she poured milk from a pink china pitcher into a tall glass, "and they've all gone to the Horse Fair."

Clara laid down her spoon with a bang.

"The Horse Fair!" she cried. "Oh, why didn't they take me?"

Mrs. Barton smiled.

"Because I asked them not to. Our new hired girl's sick today. She won't be able to help me, so you'll have to, instead."

"But I wanted to go to the Horse Fair!" Clara wailed. "And David promised he'd try to take me!"

Her mother patted her on the shoulder.

"Don't feel so badly about it, my dear," she said. "Drink your milk and eat your wheat cakes and then you can help me cut out some cookies. It's time I took you under my wing and taught you to do things in the kitchen. You're too much of a tomboy, Clara."

Clara looked glum. She finished her breakfast in silence. Then she got up from the table and walked to the kitchen window.

She didn't want to stay in this hot room when the woods beyond the pasture were flaming with leaves that were scarlet and gold. She liked to eat cookies, of course, but not to stay indoors and cut them out on a day like this.

Just then a white dog with silky ears scratched on the kitchen doorsill.

"Button!" cried Clara, opening the door. "Come on in here and stay with me! We can't go riding or even play with the ducks on the pond this morning. We have to stay inside and cut out cookies!"

Her mother spoke in a voice that meant she would take no nonsense.

"You'd better get busy now, Clara," she said.

With Button at her heels, Clara walked unwillingly back to the table and cleared away her dishes. Then she brightened at a sudden thought. When David came back from the Horse Fair, he would find a way to get her out of the kitchen! He was her favorite brother. Though he was thirteen years older than she was, he was a good companion. She could count on him for anything! With a little smile she picked up the cooky cutter.

Her mother watched her work, smiling.

"I do declare, Clara," she said, a half hour later, "you can do a right good job when you set your mind to it!"

The last batch of cookies was going into the oven some time later, when Button perked up his ears and dashed to the kitchen door. Clara's eyes shone.

"They're back!" she cried gaily. "David and Father are back from the Fair! I'm going out to meet them!"

Before her mother could give her permission, Clara was out of doors. Button scampered at her side, barking excitedly.

"David! David!" called Clara. "Oh, Father!"

"Hello, Clara!"

They waved to her from the big buckboard wagon. David was driving the team of big roans. He was a tall, broad-shouldered young man with brown eyes and a merry laugh. Everyone in the countryside liked him. Clara thought he looked very handsome in his wide-brimmed hat.

"Hi, there, Moppet!" he cried, as he brought the wagon to a stop. "Look what we have behind the wagon!"

To her delight, Clara saw that they had brought home a new fawn-colored horse. They must have bought it at the Fair! She wondered if it could be the jumper that David had set his heart upon.

Eagerly she watched David and her father untie the horse and lead it away from the wagon.

"Isn't she a beauty?" asked her father.

Clara was almost too excited to speak. She

thought this creature the loveliest she had ever seen.

The mare's coat was the tawny color of yellow sand. Her mane was long and so silky it glittered like a golden fringe. Her throat arched so beautifully that Clara knew at once that she was a thoroughbred.

"Oh!" the little girl breathed happily. "Surely you must be the jumper!"

"That she is!" said David. "Do you want to try her out with me?"

"Do I?" she exclaimed.

Her father laughed and swung her up to the horse's back. David mounted too, and took the reins with a firm but gentle hand.

"Steady, Tucky," he murmured gently.

"Tucky!" repeated Clara. "Oh, that's a nice name!"

David's eyes twinkled.

"She is called Tucky," he said, "because she hails from the state of Kentucky where thoroughbred horses are raised," he explained. After a moment, he commanded, "All right now, Tucky! Let's go!" and pressed the horse's sides lightly with his heels.

"Where are we going?" asked Clara, as she

Tucky jumped over it like a breeze

and her big brother cantered down the lane.

"Just you hang on now, Moppet," David answered gaily. "We're going over the hills and far away!"

He guided the horse toward the east meadow. When they came to a stone wall, Tucky jumped over it like a breeze.

"She's good!" cried Clara. "She's wonderful!"

Presently they came to a patch of woodland. Elms and maples aflame with autumn color stood on the shore of a lake.

"We'd better let Tucky cool off a bit." David drew the mare to a stop and swung down from her back.

Clara, too, slid down to the ground. She turned to pet the horse. Then she cocked her head to one side. A bird was chirping again and again, as if it were in trouble.

"That's funny," she said to David. "Do you suppose that bird's hurt?"

Without waiting for his answer, she walked quietly in the direction of the chirping sound. A moment later, at the foot of a willow tree near the edge of the lake, she saw a red-winged blackbird. The bird fluttered on the ground.

Slowly Clara moved closer and closer. Carefully stooping, she picked the bird up.

"Its leg is broken," she told David, as she gently stroked its shining feathers.

David looked down at her and smiled.

"Now you have another patient, Moppet," he said sympathetically, as the bird fluttered and tried to escape.

Clara nodded soberly. She knew that he meant she would take the bird home and nurse it until it was well. She loved to take care of injured birds and small animals she sometimes found in the woods. She had had many kinds to take care of. A squirrel. A raccoon. And even a little baby skunk!

"Hold the bird for me, please, David," she said. "And I'll make a nest for it out of my apron. I can carry it better that way."

The bird made a wild twittering sound as David held it firmly in his hands. Clara stroked its feathers again when he gave it back to her. Then she laid it very gently in the soft folds of her apron.

"Let's go home now, David," she said happily. "I've got a lot of work to do before this bird can fly again!"

CHAPTER TWO

Snowbound!

"THERE'LL be a blizzard tonight, I'm sure," remarked Mr. Barton. "But it's time for one, I guess. After all, it's January."

Clara was standing beside him looking out of the parlor window. She pressed her nose against the frosty pane.

"Look at the snow clouds over the woods," she said gaily. "Do you think that we'll be snowbound?"

Mr. Barton chuckled as he looked down at her eager face.

"I shouldn't be surprised!" he answered. Then he laughed. "You look as though you would like to be!"

Clara laughed too.

"Don't you think it would be fun?" She

glanced at the big open fireplace. "There are lots of logs to keep the fire roaring. We could all sit around and pop corn. And you can tell me again how you fought the Indians in the West with Mad Anthony Wayne!"

"Those were great days!" her father exclaimed. At that moment he saw the Barton carriage coming up the lane. "Here come your sisters, and your brothers, too, I hope," he told Clara. "I'm glad to have them all here before the big snow comes."

Clara ran into the hall to meet them. All four came in together—Dorothy and Sally and Stephen and David. The boys were wearing greatcoats and mufflers. The girls seemed smothered in furs.

"It's a good thing you're home!" cried Clara. "Father says there's going to be a blizzard and maybe we'll all be snowbound!"

Sally laughed as she slipped out of her brown beaver coat.

"I'd like to have a few days' vacation from teaching school," she said. Then she turned to the boys. "Why don't you two stay with us for the night instead of going home? If we're going to be snowbound let's be together."

Clara ran into the hall to meet them

"Suits me," said Stephen, smiling.

David spoke rather anxiously.

"We'll have to unharness the team and we'd better take a look at the horses in the barn." He glanced at Clara and smiled. "Want to come with us, Moppet?"

Clara nodded and hurried away to get her coat and mittens from the closet in the hall.

"I want to see that Tucky has plenty of clean straw," she called back over her shoulder.

Mrs. Barton appeared in the doorway to the kitchen.

"Don't stay too long," she warned. "Supper's ready to put on the table."

Early darkness was closing in as Clara and her brothers hastened out to the big barn. David lighted a lantern and held it up high as they went from stall to stall. Stephen bedded the carriage horses and brought them water and fresh hay.

The stock seemed quiet and contented. The cows had already been milked. Tucky and twenty other horses stood drowsily in their stalls. Even the big fiery black stallion had a sleepy look in his eyes. The little Morgan colt nickered lazily as Clara patted his velvety nose.

"It looks like they're settled for the night," said David. "We can go in to supper now."

By the time supper was over, snow was falling softly. Clara and Button stood at the window and watched it cover the countryside like a great white counterpane. It clung to the dark branches of the leafless trees and piled itself in downy drifts against walls and window sills.

"Why, Button!" Clara exclaimed. "You can't even see the pond in front of the house! Or the river in the meadow!"

Button had his paws upon the window sill. He wagged his tail and barked as if he knew exactly what she was talking about.

Meanwhile the family gathered in the parlor to sit beside the open fire. When Clara joined them, the merry crackling of the logs seemed to say, "Let it snow, let it blow, I will keep you warm!" She watched the darting flames gnawing at the apple wood.

"What do you see in the fire, Clara?" asked Dorothy. "Pictures in the flames?"

"I was thinking," answered Clara, "that this fireplace is much larger than the one in our old house. When we moved here last summer, I crawled in and measured it."

Her mother looked up from her knitting.

"I just can't realize," she said, "that we've been here almost a year. When we decided to buy this old Learned homestead, I had no idea that I would ever like it so much."

Mr. Barton smiled.

"It's just the kind of place we need," he said contentedly. "Big and roomy—three barns for livestock—and three hundred acres of land."

David grinned as he brought a corn popper from a three-cornered cupboard.

"Do you remember how surprised we were," he laughed, "when Clara helped Mr. Harris paper the walls and paint the woodwork?"

Stephen grinned too.

"And do you remember," he asked, "how mad Clara was when she reached up too high and fell into a bucket of paste?"

Clara looked at them haughtily.

"Maybe I did fall into the bucket," she said, "but I got myself right out again!"

Sally lit another oil lamp. As she placed it on the desk, she said, "I think the thing to remember is that Clara did a really good job." She turned to her little sister. "And now how about a lesson in geography, Clara?" she asked.

"But I want to help David pop corn!" Clara protested.

Her father laughed at the frown on her face.

"You can pop corn and have a lesson in geography at the same time," he said. "We'll make a guessing game out of it and all of us will play."

Clara's eyes sparkled as she knelt on the hearth rug in front of the fire.

"That will make it fun," she said.

David put the corn in the popper and Clara held it over the flames. Soon there was a sputtering sound as the hardened kernels broke into lovely yellow puffs.

"I'll get some melted butter," said Sally, rising to go into the kitchen. "I like my popcorn covered with it!"

Mr. Barton began the geography lesson as Clara popped more corn.

"Where is the Maumee River?" he asked.

No one said a word, but they all looked at Clara.

Clara looked mischievous.

"Well, if no one else seems to know," she replied, "I guess I'd better tell you. The Maumee River is in Ohio—right in the heart of the Indian country." She looked at her father and smiled. "And there was a certain place out there where a tornado had leveled a whole forest to the ground. Mad Anthony Wayne told your regiment to hide behind the fallen trees and wait for an attack by Indians—"

"Go on," said her father as she paused.

"Your regiment stayed there until the red men tried to start a regular scalping party. Then you really began to fight!" Clara added. "You chased the Indians clear out of the country and everybody called that fight the Battle of the Fallen Timbers!" Clara ended her story with a triumphant look on her face.

"Guess you're right about that one!" said Stephen as he clapped his hands.

"Now ask me another question!" Clara demanded.

Mr. Barton stroked his mustache.

"Where is the City of Brotherly Love?" he asked with a wink at David.

Clara rose from the hearth rug.

"That's an easy one," she said with scorn. "Everyone knows it's in Pennsylvania and that its name is Philadelphia!"

"Really," said Dorothy. "I think we've taught you very well, but you needn't strut like a rooster about it!"

Mr. Barton put his arm around Clara.

"Clara only struts with us," he said kindly. "She's as shy as a dove with strangers. I hope she'll overcome it, because I'm trying to teach her that shyness isn't a Barton trait."

Sally returned from the kitchen, carrying

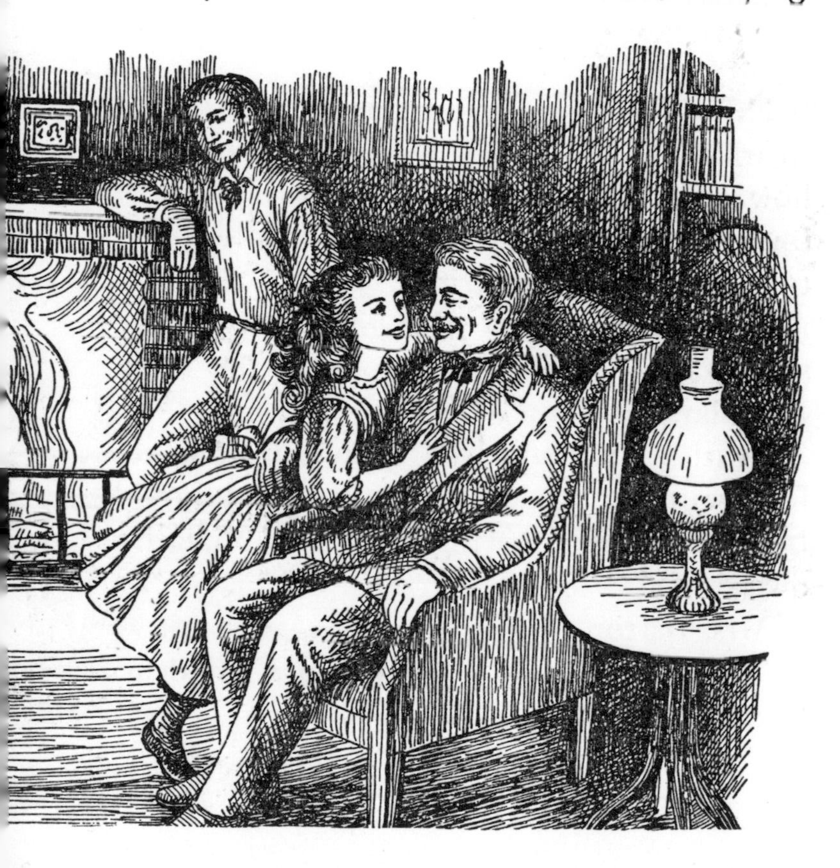

a pitcher filled with melted butter. She poured it over a bowl of popcorn.

"The wind is blowing like mad!" she said. "Listen to it! It sounds like a ghost crying in the chimney!"

While the blizzard mounted, lessons in the parlor went on. Clara learned a great deal this way, especially from her father. The two were wonderful comrades. She loved his tales of the daring men who had helped make American history.

He often told her about military campaigns in which he had taken part. He showed her how to find on maps the places where he had fought. And he taught her what it really means to be an American patriot.

Now he was about to begin a story of the stirring days which he had spent in the West. But Clara spoke up suddenly.

"I wish you had given me a pair of skates for Christmas," she said. "Round Pond should be just right for skating when this blizzard's over."

Mrs. Barton frowned.

"I don't want you to have skates, my dear. Skating is no exercise for girls!"

Clara sighed and glanced at David.

"I think it is. Don't you, David?"

David wasn't sure.

"I wouldn't want you to fall through the ice," he laughed.

Clara looked disappointed.

"Do you think I'd be stupid enough for that?" she protested. "I can climb a tree as fast as any boy and ride any horse. So why couldn't I skate? Even Lovett Stimpson thinks that I'd be good and he can skate better than anybody I know!"

Mrs. Barton frowned again.

"It's what I think that matters, Clara," she said firmly. "You can't skate, because I won't let you. And now it's time to go to bed." She folded her knitting and rose from the chair. "If I didn't suggest it, I suppose that you and the whole Barton family would sit up all night!"

With an affectionate glance at them all, Mrs. Barton began turning out lights.

CHAPTER THREE

Clara Goes Skating

EARLY the following week, the ice was just right for skating. The Learned boys and Lovett Stimpson spent all the time they possibly could skating on Round Pond.

"It's such fun!" Lovett told Clara. "The ice will be crowded with skaters tonight!"

"Yes, I guess it will," Clara agreed wistfully.

Though Lovett was just her age, he was taller than she. He leaned down to whisper in her ear.

"I could borrow a pair of skates for you," he said.

"You know I'm not allowed to skate," she told him.

Lovett smiled slyly.

"I could still borrow the skates," he whispered. "And when I go down to Round Pond tonight I could whistle under your window."

"Why—why, Lovett Stimpson!" Clara's eyes were wide with surprise.

"I could whistle," he repeated, "and it would be a signal for you to sneak out of the house."

"I couldn't. I just couldn't!" said Clara. "They won't let me skate because I'm a girl."

"You're not a girl when it comes to sports!" grinned Lovett. "You're a regular tomboy!" Then he uttered an awful challenge. "I dare you, Clara. I DARE YOU!"

Clara hesitated. She wanted to go skating with Lovett. And the worst part about it was that Lovett knew she wanted to!

"Oh, I shouldn't!" she said weakly.

Lovett's freckled face crinkled into another grin.

"I'll be here," he whispered. "And I'll whistle!"

Clara knew that he would be just as good as his word. She was in her room that night shortly after eight o'clock. From her window she could see Round Pond gleaming in the bright light of the moon. The Learned boys were already down there skating. Their mufflers were flying in the wind and they were gliding swiftly over the ice.

The Learneds had a separate entrance to the Barton house. Clara thought she heard their door being slammed. A moment later she saw Lovett stealing around through the shrubbery to stand directly under her window. There it was! His long, low whistle!

She opened the window ever so little.

"Lovett!" she called softly. "Go 'way!"

He looked up and grinned.

"I dare you!" he said in a low voice. Then

he added teasingly, "Wouldn't you like to beat me in a race on skates?"

Of course Clara wanted to beat him!

"You just wait!" she cried softly. Then she closed the window.

Her coat and bonnet and mittens lay on the rocking chair. Had she put them there just in case? Clara felt suddenly wicked.

Stealthily, she put them on. Girl or no girl, she had to show this whippersnapper of a Lovett Stimpson!

The rest of the family was in the parlor listening to David play his fiddle.

Clara's heart was pounding. She crept down the stairs one foot at a time. Then, very, very stealthily, she went out the back door.

"So you're going to beat me on skates!" teased Lovett as she walked toward him.

The shining blades of the skates he had borrowed glittered in the light of the full moon.

"Hush!" she warned him, laying her finger against her lips. "Even with David playing the fiddle, the family is liable to hear us! Let's hurry down to the pond."

As they walked across the hard-crusted snow, it crackled under their feet. Clara was tingling down to her fingertips. What fun it was to be outdoors on this winter night! How exciting it would be if she really could beat Lovett in a race around the pond!

"But I've never even been on skates," she thought in sudden despair. "So how can I hope to win?"

"Let's go this way, Clara." Lovett led the way to a spot where the Learned boys were building a fire.

"Hey! Look who's here!" The eldest of the Learned boys stared at Clara in surprise. "Look who's going to skate tonight!"

"By cracky! It's Clara!" one of the younger boys cried.

"Why not?" she asked proudly.

"I'll bet your family doesn't know about this!" another Learned boy exclaimed.

"Maybe they do and maybe they don't!" Clara said quickly.

Lovett grinned down at her.

"Sit on this log and I'll put on your skates," he said.

Clara sat down and allowed him to fasten the skates. They seemed a bit loose as she stood up and put her weight down upon them.

Clara sat down and allowed him to fasten the skates

"I think one of them is going to wobble," she told Lovett anxiously.

"I'll tighten both of them a bit," he answered. "There now! Try them again!"

Clara stood up again. The skates still felt too large, but she thought that she could manage.

"Ready?" she asked Lovett.

"Ready," he repeated, and reached for her hands. "You had better take a turn or two with me before you try skating alone."

"Hurray for Clara!" called the Learned boys as she and Lovett started off.

Clara was awkward at first. But soon she found herself gliding gracefully across the ice. Oh, this was wonderful! All you had to do was to let yourself go!

Lovett spoke with grudging admiration.

"You're good, Clara. You're really good! Want to try it alone?"

"Oh, yes!" Her eyes were sparkling like the stars that hung low in the sky.

Lovett let go of her hand and she skimmed away from him. Twice she circled Round Pond. Twice she passed the boys gathered at the bonfire. They tossed their caps in the air and cheered. Then Lovett glided to her side.

"How about that race?" he challenged.

"Let's go!" she answered merrily.

"Once around the pond," he suggested. "Get ready now. Set! Go!"

Clara really got off to a good start. For a moment she was almost abreast with Lovett, then she skated a few yards ahead. Suddenly she reached a place where the ice was rough.

The skate that had seemed to wobble when Lovett had put it on, loosened itself and turned sidewise. Clara pitched forward and fell to her knees.

"Shucks!" she said, more in angry surprise than in pain, although she could feel jagged ice cutting into her knees. "Oh, shucks!"

Lovett came back to her side the moment he saw her fall.

"What happened?" he asked anxiously, helping her to her feet. "You were going along like a breeze and then—"

"The skate came loose and dragged on the ice and down I went with a bang!" answered crestfallen Clara.

Lovett suddenly laughed.

"You needn't look so mad about it," he said. "You were doing so well, I'm sure—well, almost sure—that you would have won the race!"

"That's something, I guess," said Clara. Then, as she tried to straighten up, she cried out in pain, "Ouch! My knees!"

By this time all the boys on the pond had gathered around anxiously.

"It's a shame!" said the eldest Learned boy. "But, anyhow, Clara, you know you can skate."

"Yes, I can skate," said Clara, "but now I've got to get back to the house."

"We'll carry you," they offered.

" I can walk, thank you," Clara said firmly. "And Lovett will go along to help me."

When they had reached the house, Clara was really limping. Her woolen stockings were stained with blood.

"I think you should call your mother," said Lovett. "She'll be able to do something."

Clara looked up at the darkened windows. The family had retired for the night. Of course they thought that she had, too.

"I will not call Mother," she told Lovett. "She would be sure to scold me for going out. And if she heard I'd been skating, she'd scold me all the harder! I know how to bandage a knee and I'll fix this up in a jiffy!"

Lovett reluctantly left her climbing slowly up the back stairs. When she reached her room she examined her knees. There was a deep cut in one. She bandaged it very carefully and crept quietly into bed. Although Button lay in the rocking chair, she didn't speak a word to him. He blinked at her in surprise for a moment, then wagged his tail and went back to sleep.

All night long Clara's knee hurt. Every time she tried to bend it, the pain seemed worse than a sharp toothache. But she managed to get up for breakfast.

"I will not limp!" she told herself with determination as she went downstairs.

At first no one noticed that all was not quite well with Clara. It was not until later in the morning that Mrs. Barton saw her daughter wince as though she were in pain. And then she caught her limping!

"Clara!" she exclaimed, startled. "What's wrong with you? You're limping!"

Clara sat down on a chair at the kitchen table.

"There's nothing really wrong," she said. "I—I skinned my knee a little."

Her mother went on with her work at the kitchen stove.

"If you would learn to walk like a young lady instead of running like a tomboy," she said, "you would have fewer falls."

"If you only knew *how* I fell," thought Clara, almost crying aloud as she felt another sharp pain.

All that day she hid her suffering, but when suppertime came she couldn't walk at all!

"Call the doctor!" ordered her father.

The family doctor came in haste. He said Clara had injured her knee so badly that she must be kept off her feet for at least three weeks! And then, of course, Clara had to confess her whole adventure with Lovett!

"I guess I got what was coming to me," she said woefully.

"Perhaps," said her mother, laying her hand tenderly on Clara's shoulder. "And perhaps not. We'll just add it up to experience."

"But to stay off my feet for three whole weeks!" Clara protested. "Why, I can't even go to the barn! Glory! I'll just die!"

Mrs. Barton laughed at the tragic look on her daughter's face.

"Of course you won't die," she said. "And I can use three weeks of your time. I'll teach you how to sew."

"Sew!" echoed Clara, as though learning to sew would be a real punishment.

Mrs. Barton often sewed for the poor families of the community. Now she began to teach Clara to baste and to hem.

Clara tried hard to sew well. One morning when she was hemming a handkerchief, David teased her.

"All you need is a little lace cap and you'd look like a nice old lady, Clara," he said.

"Maybe I would," Clara answered with a smile, "but I think Mother's right. I'll need to know how to sew someday."

And "someday" indeed, she would. In a far-off country across the sea Clara would "someday" remember this morning.

CHAPTER FOUR

David Is Hurt

IT SEEMED no time at all until the ice had melted from Round Pond and spring was in the air. Crocuses spangled the grass, then lilacs burst into blossom at the Bartons' kitchen door.

Spring passed into summer which was always exciting on the Barton farm. Baby lambs grew into sheep. Long-legged calves grew into heifers. Playful colts grew into high-stepping horses.

Clara and the Learned boys and girls helped with many chores. They rode on the hay wagon and picked ripe fruit.

Fall came all too soon and school began. Lovett often carried Clara's books as they trudged along the road to the schoolhouse.

"You're a smart girl, Clara," he said one winter morning. "How you get such high marks in history and geography is beyond me!"

Clara smiled.

"I like geography, Lovett," she explained, "because someday I'm going to travel. I want to see heather growing in Scotland and the snow-crowned mountains of the Alps." Then she added eagerly, "And I like history because it tells me what has happened in all the places I want to see."

Lovett grinned and scratched his ear.

"You're pretty young to be thinking of traveling," he teased.

"I'll be eleven years old on Christmas!" Clara boasted proudly.

And Christmas seemed to be just around the corner! Soon there were jingling bells on the Barton sleigh and a glorious Christmas tree in the parlor. An angel with golden hair smiled down from the topmost branch and there were so many lighted candles that the whole room seemed aglow.

Never had Clara had such a birthday! David was waiting for her in the hall as she came down the stairs on Christmas night. She was wearing a new green satin dress with ruffles on the skirt and every ruffle was trimmed with green velvet. David looked at her proudly.

"You look pretty enough to put on the tree!" he laughed. Then he reached for her hand. "Come on outside," he invited. "Carolers are singing Christmas carols."

"Oh, how nice!" she said eagerly. "Listen! They're singing 'Joy to the World!' " She paused only long enough to get her coat and bonnet from the cupboard in the hall. "But where's the rest of the family?" she asked.

"They've already joined the singers," he answered. "Don't you hear Father's voice booming above the rest?"

They hastened out of the house on to the big front porch. Clara didn't see any carolers. And the singing sounded now as though it were coming from the barn.

"What have they gone down there for?" she asked, disappointed. "Are they singing to the horses and cows?"

"Could be!" laughed David. "Let's follow them, Moppet."

She followed him across the snow, looking very puzzled. There was no one in the barnyard, but when they went into the stable—

"Surprise!" a chorus of voices cried.

Clara could scarcely believe what she saw. All the rest of the Barton family was assembled beside one of the stalls. They were looking at a horse that she had never seen before.

"Surprise?" she questioned. Then her

eyes opened wide with delight. "For me?"

"Of course it's for you," laughed her father. "I'm giving you this horse for your birthday! You were a Christmas baby, you know."

"A horse to be all my own?" she asked him wonderingly.

"All your own, Clara," Mr. Barton answered.

"Oh, what a beauty he is!" she cried, going into the stall cautiously lest she should frighten the newcomer. "And he's a Morgan, isn't he?"

She put her arms around the thoroughbred's neck. He was almost mahogany brown in color and his coat was so shining it glistened like silk. He had a delicate head and a heavy, well-set tail.

"It's a Morgan horse, all right," said Stephen. "He's a high-stepper, too, and has lots of fire."

Clara fondled the horse lovingly.

"I'm going to call you Billy," she said. Then as she looked at the family, she added, "This is like the first Christmas night that we read about in the Bible. All the animals in the barn and everyone so happy—"

"Oh, Billy!" she breathed. "Just to think you are all my own!"

Mrs. Barton fondled Clara's curls.

"I have something that I hope will make you even happier," she said. "Look over here."

Stephen and David were bringing a saddle from a neighboring stall. It was quite an elegant saddle, hand-tooled and trimmed with silver.

"It's a sidesaddle!" exclaimed Clara, as the boys put it upon her new horse.

Mrs. Barton smiled.

"I used it myself when I was a girl, so that makes it almost an heirloom."

"An heirloom," Clara repeated softly. "Why, it's wonderful, Mother. Wonderful!"

David took Clara's hand.

"Come on now, Moppet, mount your new horse!" he said.

Clara climbed into the saddle, looking very happy.

"Oh, Billy!" she breathed. "Just to think you are all my own!"

"You look almost like a young lady, Clara," Sally said admiringly.

"You'll have to have a pretty new riding habit," added Dorothy. "The kind that fashionable young ladies wear."

"And you'd better stop being a tomboy!" warned David.

Clara looked down at him merrily.

"Just wait until spring!" she exclaimed. "Billy and I will race you and Tucky, and you'll see what kind of a tomboy I am!"

Christmas seemed scarcely over when spring came skipping after it. As soon as the hills were green, Clara and David rode their horses across the fields and through the woods.

"You're such a good companion!" Clara said to David one day. "I'm lucky to have a brother like you!"

David pulled her curls with a grin.

"You're giving me taffy, Moppet," he teased.

But Clara had meant every word of it. Every single word.

She had reason to remember this day only a few weeks later.

David was building a new barn on his own farm. Neighbors for miles around came to the barn-raising. The men brought axes and hatchets to help with the carpentry work. The women brought hampers filled with good things to eat.

Mrs. Barton had already prepared a big picnic luncheon. The table was set out of doors, loaded with delicious foods. Salads were made in big wooden bowls. Baked beans were brought from a huge outdoor oven. Coffee and milk were served in stone mugs.

After the men had set up the sides of the barn, everyone sat down to eat. Clara smiled at David from her place across the table.

"We're all waiting to watch you climb up to the ridgepole," she said. "They say no one else in the county can fix rafters to a ridgepole as well as you can."

"Taffy again?" asked David, smiling.

A man sitting next to him said:

"It's not taffy at all, young man. You're as strong as an ox and the best athlete in the countryside. Everyone knows that!"

So after the luncheon was over, everyone gathered to see David begin the work of attaching the rafters to the long ridgepole. People craned their necks as they watched him climb nimbly up to a high board which stretched from one side wall to another. It was so high that it looked to all the people who had gathered below as though it hung in space.

Clara held her breath as she saw David step out upon the board. He smiled down upon her as he balanced himself upon it and walked out toward the center.

"Careful, David! Oh, do be careful!" she called.

"He'll be all right," said Stephen, who was standing next to her. "He's done this a hundred times!"

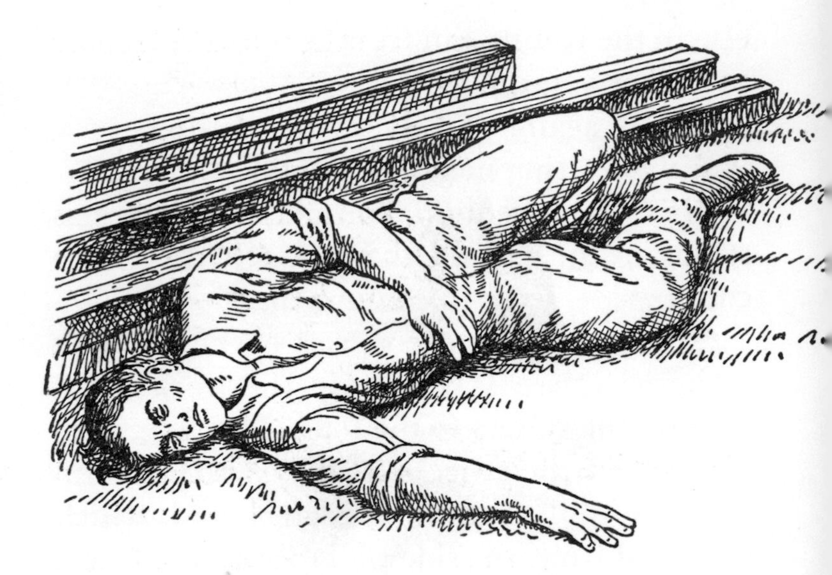

But David was not all right. Suddenly the board bent. Then it splintered with a horrible cracking sound and broke. All below gasped in horror. David was falling—falling—

Clara screamed aloud as his body hit the ground, striking heavy timbers.

"David!" she cried. "Oh, David!"

She was the first to reach him. Had he hurt himself badly? Or was he dead?

Clara asked herself these terrible questions as she knelt beside him, sobbing.

CHAPTER FIVE

A Touch of Magic

"CLARA, you ninny! Don't be a crybaby!"

David was already getting to his feet as she reached out her hand to touch him.

"But, David, you fell from way up there!" she said tearfully. "Surely you are killed!"

He laughed down at her gaily as others crowded around them.

"Do I look killed?" he asked. "Maybe I've got a few bruises, but no bones are broken, I'm quite sure."

"Lucky David!" breathed Mrs. Barton. "You don't know how thankful I am for that!"

David picked up a hammer and grinned at the men surrounding him.

"It's time we went back to work," he said.

"Are you sure you are able?" his father asked anxiously.

"Come on!" David cried, leading the way to a cider keg. "One drink of Mother's apple cider and I'll be as fit as a fiddle!"

He drank a glass of cider and rested a moment under a tree. Then he started back to the barn.

"Are you sure you're all right?" asked his father again, walking at his side.

David brushed his hand across his forehead.

"There's a little pain behind my eyes," he admitted. "But it will wear off when I start working."

David worked hard but the pain didn't wear off. The next day—the next week—the next month—it was there, nagging at him day and night.

Mrs. Barton insisted that he stay with the family in the farmhouse instead of in his own home. Then, if he became ill, someone would be near to help him.

One morning David didn't come down to breakfast.

"Do you think he's still sleeping?" Clara asked her mother anxiously.

"I don't know, dear," said Mrs. Barton, looking at the kitchen clock. "It isn't like him to sleep so late."

"I think I'll tiptoe up and see," said Clara. "Yesterday, when he thought no one was around, I saw him resting his head on his hands. And he looked so pale!"

Before Mrs. Barton could answer, Clara made her way to the stairs. She raced up two steps at a time, but when she reached the door of David's room she suddenly stopped short. Even before she went in, she could hear him groaning.

"David!" she cried, hurrying into the room, "you're sick this morning, aren't you?"

"Well, I'm not staying in bed just because I'm lazy, Moppet," David said. He attempted to smile, but suddenly his face twisted and he closed his eyes. "This infernal pain," he muttered.

Clara laid her hand on his forehead.

"You're feverish," she said. "Your forehead's awfully hot."

"I'd like a drink of water, Moppet," he said very slowly without opening his eyes.

Clara filled a glass with water from a pitcher on the washstand. She held it to his lips and told him to drink only a little at a time.

"Guess I'm weak as a sick cat!" he exclaimed, trying hard to joke. "Your big giant of a brother!"

"Lie still!" she scolded. "And don't talk! I'm going to put cold towels on your head."

She went back to the washstand and poured water from the pitcher into the china washbowl. She was soaking a fresh linen towel when her mother came into the room.

"David! You're really ill," Mrs. Barton exclaimed. "I'll tend to him, Clara."

David half opened his eyes.

"Let Clara do it, Mother," he said in a weak voice. "There's something soothing about the touch of her hands." Then he turned his head on the pillow, exhausted.

Clara gently laid cold towels on his forehead. All that day she tended to his needs. That night she brought a pallet into the room and made a bed for herself on the floor.

No one in the Barton family could coax Clara away from David's side. Although each one of them wanted to relieve her, she would allow no one to take care of him for more than a little while at a time.

"David is my patient," she said firmly. "I'm going to nurse him until he gets well."

"You're as stubborn as a little mule," her father scolded her one morning.

"But I know how to take care of David," Clara protested. "He says that I can make him more comfortable than anyone else can."

"Let her stay," David begged in a whisper.

And so Clara stayed.

The Bartons' doctor said that David had a "settled fever." He said it would last for seven days but could be helped by mustard plasters.

"I'll fix the plasters," said Clara, "and I'll give him the medicine the doctor left, according to directions."

But the mustard plasters did no good. More than seven days went by and David's pain was worse than it had ever been. Another doctor was called. He said David would have to be bled. And he taught Clara to put leeches on David's skin to draw blood from his body. This, too, failed to lessen the fever.

Everyone was worried and Clara was in despair.

"We've got to try something else," she said. "There must be *some* way to cure him."

But nothing else, including a dozen different drugs, helped David to grow better.

"There is nothing more we can do, Mr. Barton," the doctors finally announced. "Your son seems to be beyond any treatment we can give."

"That isn't true!" cried Clara. "Something can be done! I know it can, and I'll go on nursing David until it is!"

Summer passed into autumn. The doctors ceased trying to make David well.

"They think that I'm going to die," he said

weakly. "That's why they've stopped coming to see me."

Clara smoothed his hair.

"You're not going to die," she comforted him, "because I pray to God to make you well and He is too good to take you away from us."

Clara's faith raised David's spirits. When it came time for her to go back to school, she refused to go. Even Mrs. Barton was willing to let her stay at home and care for David. Everyone loved him, but he seemed to want only Clara.

"The child is amazing!" Mr. Barton said

one day to his wife. "She's only eleven years old and yet she seems to have a touch of magic in her hands when it comes to nursing."

Mrs. Barton's eyes filled with tears.

"She has a wonderful way with David. If, as life goes on, she can serve others likewise—"

Mr. Barton laid his hand on hers.

"Somehow," he said, "I think that she will."

Clara often read to David. He liked to listen to *Aesop's Fables,* parts of *Pilgrim's Progress,* and the book of *Psalms*. Sometimes he listened when he was too weary to lift his head from the pillow. Then Clara would scold him, saying: "You mustn't listen any more, David. You are too tired."

"Just read one more chapter, Moppet," he would beg.

But she would close the book firmly.

"Not even one more. You've got to rest."

She would tuck the bed covers around him and pull the window shades down to darken the room. Then she would sit quietly by, in case he should be restless. Week in, week out, she was always there, as still as a sleepy kitten. Months passed in this way.

"Clara is growing as pale as David," Mrs.

Barton said one evening. "I am almost as worried about her as I am about him."

Mr. Barton nodded understandingly.

"I must scour the country for new doctors," he said. "Surely there is someone—somewhere—"

Early one morning when Clara was still in her white embroidered nightdress, she heard footsteps on the stairs. Who could be coming to see David so early, she wondered? The family rarely came until after breakfast.

She threw a pink knitted shawl around her small shoulders. A moment later, the door to the bedroom was opened and her father stood on the threshold. A stranger stood beside him.

"This is Dr. Asa McCullum, Clara," said her father. "He has come to see David and will use a new and different method to treat him."

The doctor looked at Clara and smiled.

"You are such a little girl," he said, "to carry on this big job of nursing."

Clara smiled shyly and led him over to David's bed. "Please make him well," she half-whispered.

Although it was more than a year since David had fallen from the ridgepole, Dr. Mc-

"Please make him well," she half-whispered

Cullum was the first doctor who knew how to treat that pain behind David's eyes.

After he had examined his patient, he took him away to a sanitarium.

"Clara is to stay at the sanitarium with him just as much as she wants to," he told the Barton family. "If it had not been for her constant attention, David might have died."

After three weeks' treatment under Dr. McCullum's care, David took a turn for the better. In three more weeks, he was out of bed.

"Soon," he said gaily to Clara, "we'll be riding across the fields again."

Clara smiled at the prospect. Oh, how good it would be to ride over the hills with David well and strong again!

David was watching her soberly.

"Father is right about you, Moppet," he said. "You seem to have a touch of magic in your hands when it comes to nursing. It was you who pulled me through. Even Dr. McCullum says so."

Clara spoke with shining eyes. "I had to pull you through, David," she said. "Magic or no magic! I just had to pull you through because —well, because you're David!"

CHAPTER SIX

The Little Schoolmarm

TIME hung heavy on Clara's hands after David's recovery. She was glad to get back to school, and she studied hard. Then the weeks passed more quickly. At last the day came when she knew she must decide what to do when she had finished school.

"Sally and Dorothy liked being teachers," she thought. "I think I'd like it, too."

Once Clara Barton made up her mind to do something, she wasted no time in carrying it out. Before long she had passed her teacher's examinations.

"But you're too young and pretty for a schoolmarm," teased David.

They were both astride their horses in front of the little stone schoolhouse where Clara was to teach. It was only a mile or two out from North Oxford.

"I'm almost sixteen," Clara answered, smiling under her rose-trimmed bonnet. "It's time that I wore long skirts and put up my hair!" She slid down from her saddle and hurried to the schoolhouse door. "Come on in and see the schoolroom," she called. "I've got a key!"

They went inside as excited as children exploring a cavern by the sea. There was only one big classroom.

"Here are the desks for the younger children," Clara said, as she pointed them out to David. "And those larger ones to the rear are for the older girls and boys."

David looked around with a smile.

"It's a nice large classroom," he said. "And there's a lot of blackboard space. That's something a teacher really needs."

"And look at my desk up here on the platform!" Clara said. "I've made the chair high so I'll look more than five feet tall!"

David laughed at her gaily.

"I'll wager some of your pupils will look like giants compared to you, Moppet! How in the world will you manage them?"

"And look at my desk up here on the platform"

"I am scared inside," she admitted. "But I'll never let them find it out!"

It seemed very hard, however, to appear unruffled on the day that school started. On that bright Monday morning forty scholars stood staring at Clara from behind the rows of desks. Forty girls and boys! Some of them were sober, especially the younger children. Others were curious. And one big, lanky boy seemed to be mocking the new teacher, with laughing lips and eyes.

Clara stood up very straight. She hoped that she looked tall.

"Good morning, class," she managed to say in a nice clear voice.

"Good morning, Miss Barton." They all chimed the words at once.

"You may take your seats," she said, smiling.

All of them obeyed her, but the big boy snickered. Clara knew she must not let that snicker go by. If she did, she would appear weak in the eyes of the class, even before she had started teaching!

"What is your name?" she asked the boy coldly.

"Edwin Gates," he said with a swagger.

"Come up here, Edwin," she ordered. "I have something to say to you."

The boy dawdled up the aisle between the desks until he reached the teacher's platform. Suddenly he looked angry and started to grumble under his breath.

"Well?" he finally said, looking at her defiantly.

Clara suddenly smiled.

"You're a big boy, Edwin Gates," she said. "But somehow I don't think you are quite as big as you think you are."

"I can throw a horse!" he boasted, while many of his classmates laughed.

Again Clara smiled.

"Maybe you can," she acknowledged, "but can you bow to a lady?"

"Bow to a lady!" he exclaimed, as though she had asked him to fly to the moon!

Another smile from Clara.

"A boy as tall as you are looks like a young man," she said. "And young men mind their manners. They bow to a lady, Edwin, and they never snicker."

Edwin stood silent, at a loss for words.

"And if they do snicker," Clara continued, "they are merely bad little boys and no one respects the strength they lay claim to." She walked around from the back of her desk and looked up at him in a friendly way. "Do you know what I mean?"

He saw a twinkle in her eyes.

"Guess I do, Miss Barton," he said with a sudden smile, "but—bowing! Oh, shucks!"

"Want to try it?" she challenged.

All the scholars laughed as Edwin bent awkwardly from the waist, but Clara applauded him warmly.

"Why, that's a beautiful bow!" she cried. "You see, you are a fine young man, so we'll forget about that snicker!"

Clara knew she had gained a point. She wanted to make friends with these boys and girls—with every single one of them—even Edwin Gates!

He was still standing in front of her, looking sheepish.

"One of these days, Edwin," she said merrily, "I'll watch you throw a horse. I'm sure that you are strong enough to do it with great ease."

Edwin looked pleased. She wasn't making him out to be a ninny in front of the class after all! He guessed that she was going to be a very good sport!

"Thank you, Miss Barton," he said, almost gratefully.

"You may go back to your seat now." Clara smiled and turned back to her desk. "And now, class," she said, picking up a well-worn Bible. "I think we'll read by turns, 'The Sermon on the Mount.' "

Before many weeks had passed, all the children loved Clara Barton. She knew how to make them want to learn. When she described a battle to the history class, they could almost hear the sound of bugles and the clash of swords.

And something else surprised them. She played with them! Sometimes she played rough games with the boys. At other times she played quiet games with the little girls. She outran the best runner in the class. She could ride a fast horse better even than Edwin Gates. And there wasn't anyone in the school whom she couldn't beat when it came to pitching horseshoes!

The children were sorry to have school end, and when the year was over everyone agreed that Clara Barton was the best teacher for miles around. So she continued teaching.

At first she taught in schools near home. Then she went to Bordentown, Now Jersey. There was no public school in Bordentown. Clara was dismayed to see how many children roamed the streets all day and how few were learning to read and write and figure. She decided that she would like to start a public school.

"But a public school here is impossible,"

said the people of Bordentown. "Many of the children you have seen on the streets are just little ragamuffins. You can't mix them with nice children of wealthier families."

"I think I can," Clara Barton replied. "Just give me three months in which to try. And during that time I will teach the children for nothing."

At last the people of Bordentown permitted her to start a public school in a tumbledown building. She had only six pupils when the school opened. But in five weeks the building was too small to hold all the children who came.

The school grew rapidly and the work was difficult, but Clara kept on teaching for several years. Even when she had an assistant, she was often worn out at the end of the day. At length she became so tired that she was barely able to speak.

"If you do not want to lose your voice entirely, Miss Barton, you must give up teaching," her doctor told her. "You must rest."

"Just rest!" exclaimed Clara gloomily. "That will be awful!"

The doctor looked at her sternly.

"Get something else to do then," he said. "Perhaps you could work with your hands."

Clara sighed and looked down at her pretty hands.

"Work with my hands," she repeated. "Why, I know what I'll do!"

"Yes?" asked the doctor, smiling.

Clara's eyes were suddenly sparkling under her flower-trimmed bonnet.

"My married sister, Sally, now lives in Washington, D. C.," she told him. "I remember her saying that clerks are needed there to copy reports for the government."

"So you think you'll try it?" the doctor asked.

"Yes, I think I will," she said, picking up her parasol. "Since you say that I must work with my hands, I think I shall go to Washington!"

CHAPTER SEVEN

Clara Goes to Washington

CLARA BARTON arrived in Washington eager to make a new life for herself. She decided that she was not going to be disappointed because she could no longer teach school. Surely there were other interesting things to do in Washington in 1854!

Her sister Sally planned to take her sightseeing.

"I want you to see the whole city, Clara," she said as they sat in her flower garden one evening. "Many government buildings are only half completed. But when they are finished Washington will be the most beautiful city in the world!"

Clara's eyes were glowing.

"It's going to be fun to be in Washington,"

she said merrily. "I'll stay with you a month or two and we'll have a wonderful time sight-seeing! Then I'll find a place of my own to live in."

Sally looked displeased.

"You'll do no such thing!" she protested. "I want you to stay here with me. So do my husband and my sons!"

But in spite of Sally's protest, Clara carried out her program. After visiting with Sally, she found a large apartment in a house on T Street. And she also found a job as a clerk in the United States Patent Office. She liked her work and she enjoyed living in Washington.

"Washington is a wonderful city," she said one day to Mary Blake, who was also a government clerk. They were standing on Pennsylvania Avenue with Mrs. Blake's eight-year-old son, Jimmy.

"Yes, Washington's a wonderful city and this is a wonderful day!" said Jimmy's mother. "I was hoping it would be, because the President-elect will be riding in an open carriage."

"Look!" cried Jimmy, as Clara was about to speak. "Here comes a policeman to keep us on the sidewalk!"

Pennsylvania Avenue was lined with eager people. They were waiting to see the man who was to become the next President of the United States.

"His name is Abraham Lincoln, isn't it, Miss Barton?" Jimmy said.

Clara's eyes sparkled as she heard distant music.

"That's right, Jimmy," she said. "And he comes from Springfield, Illinois."

"Abraham Lincoln," repeated Jimmy. Then he tugged at his mother's sleeve. "Listen!" he cried. "I hear bugles blowing!"

The date was March 4, 1861. The bugles were blowing to announce the approach of soldiers on horseback who were leading the Presidential procession.

"What beautiful horses!" cried Clara, thinking of those on the Barton farm. "There's one that looks like Black Stallion and another that's the image of my own Billy!"

The horses pranced as they came up the street. The soldiers mounted upon them were wearing bright blue uniforms trimmed with gold braid. There were outriders too. Their horses seemed to be dancing to the music.

Horns blared. Big bass drums rumbled. And the drum major swung his stick with such pride that Jimmy exclaimed: "I think I'll be a drum major some day!"

Mrs. Blake glanced down at him and smiled. "Here comes the state carriage!" she said.

And then they saw Abraham Lincoln. He was nodding to the people, as high-stepping horses drew the carriage slowly toward the Capitol. Clara Barton watched Mr. Lincoln closely. "He looks very tired," she said.

"And worried, too," added Mary Blake sympathetically.

Abraham Lincoln had good reason to look worried. A great trouble had come to the United States. A trouble which was dividing the country. It had started over the question of slavery.

Many people in the Southern states owned slaves and believed that they had the right to take their slaves wherever they pleased. Many people in the North believed that all men should be free. They did not want to see slaves taken into the new territories which were being settled in the western part of the country. So a quarrel between the states had started. It was rapidly growing worse.

"Did you know that seven Southern states have already withdrawn from the Union?" Mary Blake asked as the crowd cheered Mr. Lincoln.

Clara nodded and turned away from the edge of the sidewalk.

"Let's try to follow the carriage," she suggested. "I'd like to hear Mr. Lincoln speak."

They made their way slowly toward the beautiful Capitol building until they stood at

"I'd like to hear Mr. Lincoln speak"

the foot of the East Capitol steps. Mr. Lincoln had already begun to make his inaugural address. She heard him say in his high voice:

"One section of our country believes slavery is right and ought to be extended, while the other believes it is wrong and ought not to be extended."

He paused as the people tried to get closer to the platform. They were straining to hear every word he said. After a few minutes Jimmy tugged at Clara's skirt.

"I can't understand him, Miss Barton. What's he talking about?"

"He's saying that the Union must not be broken up," Clara Barton explained hastily. "He's saying that the quarrel between the states can be settled peacefully if the people will be patient. He's asking them not to begin a civil war."

"War!" Jimmy repeated excitedly.

But Clara Barton did not hear him. She was listening intently to the tall man on the platform. There were tears in her eyes as Mr. Lincoln finished speaking. Somehow she knew that she had been listening to the voice of a great man. Surely he had been chosen by God to lead his country through these difficult times.

Jimmy was tugging at her hand.

"Look, Miss Barton," he was saying, "the man in the black robe is holding up the Bible!"

The man was Chief Justice Taney, ready to administer the solemn oath of office. Mr. Lincoln put his hand upon the open Bible and took the oath that made him the President of the United States.

Again Jimmy spoke:

"His hands are awful big, Miss Barton."

Clara smiled down at him with affection.

"They are rail-splitter's hands," she told him. "Abraham Lincoln's parents were poor. He grew up in a log cabin and has had to work very hard all his life."

"Well, now, that he's President," burst out Jimmy, "he'll—"

Clara tousled Jimmy's hair.

"He'll have to work harder than ever," she said.

But little did Clara know how hard the task would be for Mr. Lincoln, and for the people of the North and South—and for herself.

A few weeks after President Lincoln had taken office, the eyes of the whole country were anxiously turned upon a fort in Charleston Harbor, South Carolina.

"It is feared that the South will attack Fort Sumter!" Clara read in the newspaper.

"If that should happen," she said to Mary Blake, who was peering over her shoulder, "war will be declared between the states!"

"Let's pray that it won't," said Mary, troubled.

In spite of their hopes, and the hopes of thousands of others, the very next morning the big guns were fired. The South was bombarding Fort Sumter! Fifty cannon were spitting fire against its outer walls.

And later Clara read in the paper:

"This is the first blow of civil war. Gallant Fort Sumter has fallen!"

She turned a tragic face to Mary Blake.

"This means that boys are being wounded, and many of them will be killed!" she cried.

"I'm afraid it does," said Mary sadly.

Clara dashed angry tears away from her eyes.

"This is no time to be working in a patent

office!" she exclaimed. "Surely there is something we can do to help!"

Mary looked at her soberly.

"I don't know what it would be," she said.

Clara was silent as she stared at a tulip tree in blossom beyond an open window. Finally she spoke.

"I helped David when he was hurt," she said. "Father said I seemed to have a touch of magic in caring for the sick." Suddenly her eyes were shining. "If I did that for David," she went on, "surely I could do it for boys hurt on a battlefield."

Mary stared at her friend. She was thinking there was something strong-willed and determined about Clara Barton.

"Somehow," she said, looking at Clara with serious eyes, "somehow, I think that you will!"

CHAPTER EIGHT

Off to the Battle Zone

"WAR has begun!"

The news traveled swiftly throughout the country. In the North and in the South, men said good-by to their families and hurried to enlist. Soon another state broke away from the Union. Many people in Washington were terrified.

"Virginia has seceded!" they told one another. "Now the enemy is just across the river! Washington may be attacked at any moment!"

Hundreds of frightened people packed up their belongings and fled to the North. Clara Barton said good-by to Mary Blake and Jimmy, but she refused to go with them to a safer place. As soon as they had left, she hurried to her sister's house. She found Sally sitting in her pretty parlor. There was a sewing basket in her lap, but she was not sewing. A look of anxiety darkened her eyes as she rose to greet Clara.

"I wish you hadn't come!" she said. "It's not safe for you to be walking on the streets now. Haven't you heard that Washington may be attacked at any moment by soldiers from the South?"

"Of course I've heard it," said Clara. "But there's little we can do yet."

Sally sighed impatiently.

"Clara Barton!" she declared. "You were always so matter-of-fact about things, even as a child! I used to get so mad at you when you took chances on riding the fastest horses on Father's farm—but now that you're grown up, you make me even madder! You don't seem to care what kind of chance you take!"

"What have I done now?" Clara asked with a smile, as she took off her bonnet.

"Done!" Sally echoed. "I tell you that Washington may be attacked at any moment and you meekly say, 'There's little we can do yet!' " Sally's eyes flashed with fire as she added,

"Suppose the Rebels really attack the city? Suppose they burn down our houses and kidnap our children? No one will be safe!"

Clara suddenly smiled.

"Surely, Sally, you're not afraid!" she teased. "Are you going to flee with the others?"

"Are you?" asked Sally.

"No," replied Clara firmly. "If Washington is really attacked, women will be badly needed to care for the sick and wounded of both sides. If an attack really comes, I want to be where our boys are, to do what I can to help them. Don't you remember how I took care of David when he was so ill?"

Sally's eyes softened as she laid her hand on Clara's arm.

"Of course I remember—and I will all my life."

"Did you know," added Clara, "that President Lincoln has sent out a call for seventy-five thousand volunteer soldiers? Boys will be pouring into the city from every anti-slave state in the Union."

"And you'll be at the station to meet them, I suspect!" Sally said grimly.

"I, and hundreds of others!" answered Clara with a smile.

And later, as Sally suspected, Clara was at the station, standing in the crowd, when trains came puffing in from Baltimore. Tired soldiers got off. She looked at one group of weary boys and was scarcely able to believe what she saw.

"Those are my own boys!" she cried softly. "The ones I taught in school!"

She approached one eagerly.

"Aren't you young Simon," she said, "who lives on the farm next to my brother David?"

He looked at her, smiling, as he leaned on his musket.

"Why, if it isn't Miss Clara Barton!" he exclaimed. Then he called to his comrades, "Hey, fellows! Come here!"

A score of young men gathered around her. She recognized more than a dozen! One threw his arms around her and gave her a big hug. She laughed up into his face and said:

"Well, I declare! It's Edwin Gates! Remember the day you laughed at me for trying to be your teacher?"

Edwin lifted her off her feet.

Edwin lifted her off her feet

"I remember how you put me in my place!" he replied, grinning.

Suddenly she saw young men on stretchers being carried off the train.

"Who are they?" she asked Edwin.

He looked very sober.

"Didn't you know, Miss Barton?" he asked. "We were mobbed by civilians in Baltimore. Thirty of our men were injured and three were killed."

"No, I didn't know," said Clara.

She walked across the platform and bent down above the stretcher of one young lad. His eyes sought hers pitifully.

"I'm cold," he said weakly. "I'm very cold."

Clara was wearing a knitted shawl made of soft blue wool, and very warm. She took it off and tucked it around the shivering patient.

"There now," she comforted him. "This ought to help."

In a few more moments, ambulances arrived to take the wounded boys to the Washington Infirmary.

Clara turned to the group of young men still surrounding her.

"There must be many things you need,"

she said. "Tell me what they are and I will try to get them."

Edwin Gates laughed.

"We need everything, Miss Barton, from needles and pins to towels and blankets. And, of course, good things to eat!"

"Wait until I make a list!" Clara said.

Taking a pencil and notebook from her handbag, she began to write the items down. Edwin was about to tell her more things to add to the list when an officer shouted a sharp command: "All right, men! On your way!"

As the soldiers moved on, bystanders followed. The men marched to the grounds of the Capitol where they were to be stationed. Clara trudged along beside them. Everyone was excited and glad that soldiers had arrived to defend Washington in case of attack.

That afternoon Clara ransacked her linen closet. When she had finished, it looked as bare as Mother Hubbard's cupboard. Washcloths and towels, a half-dozen blankets, thimbles and scissors, needles and pins—all these she packed into boxes to take to the boys on Capitol Hill.

Then she called on Sally.

"Give me all that you and your friends can spare," she pleaded. "The boys need them badly."

Finally she went to the market. The stalls were filled with tempting things to eat. Apples and cherries. Sugar-cured hams and cold roast chickens. Golden-brown bread still warm from the oven. Chocolates and peppermints in shining glass jars!

"Just what the boys would relish!" thought Clara as she bought all she could carry.

The next morning was Sunday, but there was rejoicing on Capitol Hill. Clara entered the Senate Chamber like a queen bringing treasures to her boys. She was followed by five porters who carried large hampers filled with supplies she had collected and with the good things to eat.

The young men crowded around her as she began to distribute food.

"This is like a picnic!" they said.

Clara watched them with shining eyes.

"Tell me," she finally asked, "do you know where you are going from here?"

"I think we'll get orders to move into Virginia," Edwin Gates answered.

Several days later the men from Massachusetts left Washington and marched farther south. Clara knew that they would fight hard and that many would be sent back badly wounded or ill.

"Please, God," she prayed, "show me how I may be able to help care for them as I cared for David."

She went to several hospitals in Washington and asked to be assigned to the nursing staff.

"But we have too many nurses now!" she was told.

"If you cannot use me here, send me to the battlefields," she begged at last.

A woman on the battlefields! Army officers looked amazed. Was little Miss Clara Barton quite out of her mind?

So she went to work as a volunteer nurse wherever her services were needed in hospitals and infirmaries. At the same time she began collecting supplies for the troops.

It occurred to her to put an advertisement in a Massachusetts newspaper, asking for bandages, clothing, food, and money. She wrote to other newspapers. She begged from her friends. Soon her rooms were filled to overflowing with boxes, baskets, and bundles. There were so many that she had to move some of them into a warehouse until the time came to distribute them.

Meanwhile she received sad news from her home in North Oxford. Her father was seriously ill and needed her.

"I will take care of Father first," she told her sister Sally, who had come to the station to bid her good-by. "Then I'll return to Washington and try again to be sent to the battlefields."

Although she nursed her father tenderly, Mr. Barton steadily grew worse. Before he died, Clara told him of her wish to help the soldiers on the battlefields. The fine old patriot laid his hand on hers.

"Go, if you feel it is your duty to go," he

said. "I know soldiers. They will respect you and your errand."

That settled the matter for Clara Barton. When she returned to Washington she tried in every way she could to get permission to go where men were fighting. But no army officer would allow her to go to the battlefields. Often she was filled with despair. Would she never be allowed to do what she felt she *must* do?

The war was now being fought in the swamps of the Chickahominy River. Wounded soldiers were being returned to Washington every day. Clara felt that she must do more than give out supplies at the warehouse. She began to go down to the docks on the Potomac River, taking other volunteer nurses with her.

When boatloads of wounded men arrived, the nurses were ready with warm water, lotions, and dressings. The sun was hot in Washington, but under its fierce rays, they washed and bandaged the neglected wounds of these soldiers. Then Clara would see them to hospital beds and return once more to the river.

Many of the men died.

"They might have been saved if they had not had to wait so long for care," Clara said again and again. "The place to bind up wounds is on the battlefield."

One day she talked about this with an army officer named Rucker.

"But you are so little," he said kindly, "to want to handle so big and dangerous a job!"

"I have no fear of the battlefields," she told him. "I have large stores of supplies but no way to reach the troops. Please," she pleaded with him. "Find a way for me to go to the front lines!"

General Rucker looked down at her admiringly.

"Perhaps a little woman with so great a heart *should* serve upon the battlefields," he thought. Then he smiled.

"I myself will give you a passport to go to the front, Miss Barton," he said. "And may God bless you and your work."

"Thank you, General Rucker, and thank God!" Clara cried softly.

The call had come and she was ready. On a hot July day she climbed to the seat of a big wagon which was loaded with supplies. The driver cracked his whip. The mules pulled at the traces—and Clara Barton was off at last.

CHAPTER NINE

In the Valley of Antietam

IT WAS September 15, 1862. Clara Barton stood in the shadow of an army wagon, listening to the soldiers sing.

The men were huddled around blazing campfires. Beyond the circle of light she could see a row of white tents. These were ready to serve as shelters for the wounded when the battle began.

"Some of the soldiers are only boys—young boys," Clara said to herself. "And by this time tomorrow, many will be dead."

Sometimes she thought she could no longer bear it. To see boys wounded, suffering, dying. She had learned by now how cruel war was, and how terrifying. She had nursed men on the battlefield at Cedar Mountain in Virginia,

Sometimes she thought she could no longer bear it

where the Northerners had been defeated. She had cared for the wounded after the second battle of Bull Run near Washington.

Tonight she was in Maryland. The Union troops were in camp opposite the Confederate soldiers. Only the Valley of Antietam lay green and dark between them. And quiet. Strangely quiet.

Green and dark and quiet! But tomorrow! At dawn, the bugles would blow and the battle would begin.

"Miss Barton," a boy's voice spoke behind her.

Clara knew whose voice it was.

"Yes, Reddy," she said, turning. "What is it?"

Reddy was a water boy, fifteen years old. He, too, had been serving the Union troops in battle after battle. His face was freckled and he had brick-red hair for which he was named. He was a tall boy for his age, and a very brave one. Clara Barton had seen him go to the aid of wounded soldiers under fire many times.

He was standing beside the army wagon.

"Shall we begin unloading?" he asked. "You've brought such a lot of supplies."

Clara Barton smiled at him affectionately. "Thank you, Reddy, but we're not unloading tonight. One hundred and sixty thousand men are camped in this valley and we have no way of telling yet just where the battle will begin. Wherever General Hooker decides to open fire will be the best point, but we'll have to wait and see."

Reddy held up his hand.

"Listen, Miss Barton," he said, sounding worried. "The cavalry horses are restless."

Clara listened. Then she said soberly: "I can hear them stomping, Reddy. It's because the men are singing. War horses know war songs by instinct. They know that tomorrow will be a bad day."

"It will be worse than all the others, I guess," said Reddy. "There are so many thousands of men. I only hope we'll have enough stretcher-bearers."

"And enough supplies," added Clara. Then she laid her hand on his shoulder. "Get some sleep now, Reddy, or the big guns will be sounding off long before you know it."

"You had better sleep, too, Miss Barton," Reddy said with a smile. "I never saw a lady who could keep on the go the way you do!"

Clara Barton laughed.

"Keeping on the go is what keeps me strong," she said.

And she felt that this was true. She had had to keep on the go, in order to gather and distribute the many supplies needed by an army.

Towels, sheets, bandages, and medicines. She had brought along great stores of them. Some had come from the Quartermaster's Department in Washington. Others had been taken from the warehouse space she had rented months earlier. Housewives near Washington had added to her treasured stock, giving her blankets and cloth for dressings. Jars of apple jelly and berry jam and tons of preserves had found their way from Yankee kitchens to Clara Barton's army wagon of supplies.

Her wagon was often drawn by mule teams. It had become a familiar sight on highways and byways leading to the battlefields. Although many army officers still felt that no woman should serve in a battle area, the soldiers now welcomed Clara Barton everywhere she went. They had come to know that she would be on call with the supplies they needed most. And not only with supplies, but with gentle hands to nurse their wounds.

So, tonight, at Antietam, she stood ready.

"Which side will win tomorrow?" she was asking herself with anxiety. "Rebels or Yankees?"

As Reddy stole away into the shadows, Clara Barton bowed her head and prayed. Then she, too, tried to snatch some sleep.

She was awakened by the voices of big guns. Boom! Boom! Boom! Sunrise was lighting the valley. Minutes before, the bugles had blown, calling all men to battle.

A few moments later Clara Barton stood high on the seat of her wagon. She was watching the Northern troops through a pair of field glasses. The battle was beginning that was to be the turning point of the war. If General Lee's Rebels were to win, he would be able to push northward into Pennsylvania or even to strike Baltimore. But if Lee lost to the Yankees, he would have to return to Virginia.

Clara Barton spoke crisply.

"General Hooker has opened fire," she told Reddy and her group of field workers. "And Burnside is sending the cavalry and artillery to his aid." She dangled the field glasses in her hand and added, "I think we had better follow Burnside. Casualties will be heaviest where his men join Hooker's."

Reddy climbed up to the wagon seat and took the reins in his hands. Clara seated herself beside him as her aides climbed into the back of the wagon.

"Giddap, mules, and make time!" cried Reddy.

He cracked his whip and they were off.

They followed the threatening line of artillery for almost eight miles. The roar of mighty guns made it difficult for them to talk together. The firing of the cannon was a fearful thing to hear.

"There's a house, Reddy!" cried Clara at last.

"Where, Miss Barton?"

"Turn into that cornfield! There's a house and a barn too!"

Reddy reined in the mules.

"But, Miss Barton!" he protested.

"Don't dawdle!" she ordered. "Turn into that cornfield!"

"But, Miss Barton," Reddy repeated, "that house is almost under that last gun in Hooker's line! There's only a garden wall between them! If we work in there we'll be bombarded sure!"

"Then we'll be bombarded," Clara said calmly. "It's the only possible place. And the boys need our help here and now!"

Reddy realized that she was determined to

work as close to the firing as she could get. And one of the generals had told him to be sure to take good care of Miss Barton! Would she ever listen to anyone? Reddy sighed as he drove the wagon along a narrow road that led through the cornfield up to the house.

Clara Barton jumped down from the wagon the moment the mules stood still. She flew into the house. Before Reddy could unhitch the mules, she was coming out again.

"We'll have to work fast!" she called to the field workers. "Dr. Dunn is in the house. I worked with him at the Battle of Bull Run and I'm so glad he's here. He's already operating on the wounded and he needs stimulants and bandages at once!"

Everyone commenced to work. By ten o'clock that morning, almost three hundred men lay near the barn, badly hurt.

Reddy, as water boy, passed among them. He comforted them, saying: "Here's cool water. Drink! And don't worry about your wounds, because you'll be taken care of."

"But how?" asked one suffering corporal. "We are so many!"

Reddy looked up smiling, as Clara Barton joined them.

"Here is Miss Barton who has brought you medicine and supplies," he said. "She'll tell you how."

Clara Barton knelt beside the dark-haired lad.

"Reddy is right," she told him. "You will be taken care of. Dr. Dunn is working in that house. He is one of the finest surgeons I have ever met."

The young corporal tossed and moaned. When he turned on his side, Clara saw that his right cheek was wounded.

"Lady!" he implored, "something burns me here." He held up his hand to his cheek. "Can you tell what it is?"

She examined his face carefully.

"There's a bullet lodged in the bone," she said.

"It pains me dreadful!" said the corporal. "Won't you take it out?"

Clara Barton had never operated on anyone.

"I can't take it out," she said sadly. "I am not a surgeon. You'll have to wait your turn with Dr. Dunn."

"Dr. Dunn is busy with boys worse off than I am," said the corporal. "Won't you please try to help me?"

Clara was dismayed.

"But I would have to hurt you more than you are hurt now," she objected.

He tugged weakly at her sleeve.

"I can stand it," he said. "Just try to get that bullet out!"

Clara Barton watched him for a moment. It might be hours before his turn would come with Dr. Dunn! And perhaps she could relieve his suffering. At last she took her pocket knife out of a bag which she wore at her waist, and prepared to do the best she could.

"I'll try to be very careful," she said, beginning to probe into the flesh with the blade.

"Thank you, Miss Barton! Oh, thank you!" The weary corporal gritted his teeth, trying hard to bear the pain.

Not many minutes later, the delicate job was done. Reddy stood by with a basin of water as Miss Barton washed the blood from the boy's face and bandaged up the wound.

Meanwhile, a messenger came hurrying to her side. He took one look at the corporal.

"This boy's regiment has been cut to pieces!" he announced. "The captain was the last officer left, and now he is dead!"

The corporal looked at Clara Barton.

"Dead?" he said weakly. "All of them? And only I am alive?"

"Yes, and I thank God that you are!" said Clara Barton.

And still the guns were roaring in the Valley of Antietam.

CHAPTER TEN

Lanterns in the Field

ALL day the battle raged. All day Clara Barton and her field workers tended to the soldiers. Food was cooked and carried to the men on the battle lines.

That afternoon, supplies ran low. One of the field workers came to report that the last loaf of bread had been cut, and the last cracker pounded into meal. Only three boxes of bottled wine remained unopened!

"Open those boxes!" ordered Clara. "And God help us find more food!"

Young Sergeant Field stepped forward and opened one of the boxes. Suddenly his face was bright.

"Look, Miss Barton," he called. "A miracle has happened!"

She and Reddy, who was working near by, rushed to his side. They discovered that the wine bottles had been packed in finely sifted Indian meal!

"God has heard our prayers for these hungry men!" Clara said gratefully.

"What shall we do with the meal?" Sergeant Field asked.

"We'll make hot gruel," said Clara. Then suddenly she had an idea. "This is an old farmhouse," she added. "Suppose we explore the cellar. Sometimes fleeing housewives leave good things to eat."

Reddy looked apprehensive.

"There may be Johnny Rebs down there!" he cried.

"And so there may," said Clara, "but I'd rather meet a Rebel than see a Union soldier weak from hunger."

"I'll come with you, Miss Barton," Reddy said bravely.

"Come if you like," she answered, "but I will lead the way!"

The door to the cellar was locked. Sergeant Field pounded it open with the end of his rifle.

"Ooh! How dark it looks down there!"

cried Reddy. Then he picked up a club from the kitchen floor. "Now I'm armed," he laughed. "Let's go!"

The stairs were dark and creaking. Below them, the cellar looked like a dungeon. Once they were down the steps, however, Clara opened a side window. Sunlight flooded the mud floor.

"Here are three barrels and a bag," said Clara. "Call Sergeant Field to open them, Reddy."

When Sergeant Field had opened the barrels, they found them filled with flour, and the bag was full of salt. All bore the marks of General "Stonewall" Jackson's Rebel army.

"Old Stonewall must have left these supplies when he came through here with his scouts to plan this particular battle," beamed Clara. "What wonderful bread this will make for our men!"

She ordered that the barrels of flour be taken to the barn.

"The barn, Miss Barton?" asked Sergeant Field in surprise.

Clara Barton sighed as she explained.

"This house is so full of the wounded that

"Here are three barrels and a bag," said Clara

Dr. Dunn has scarcely space enough to work. He needs the kitchen, so we will work in the barn. We can use it and the barnyard. We'll build our fires in the barnyard and make the gruel outdoors."

Clara rolled up her sleeves to cook as she had been taught to do in her mother's New England kitchen.

For hours on end, she made hot gruel. For hours on end, her workers carried it in buckets down the battle lines. When evening came, she worked by the light of lanterns she had brought to the barn.

Once, after dark, she went to the barn door. What was wrong at the house, she wondered? Surely the surgeon was still at work, but there seemed to be no light!

She hurried to the house, her heart filled with anxiety. Had it been captured by Rebels? Had something happened to Dr. Dunn?

She found him sitting alone at a table lighted by a bit of a tallow candle, looking most discouraged.

"Are you in trouble, Dr. Dunn?" she asked.

"Trouble!" he snapped. "Yes, I'm in trouble, Miss Barton."

"Perhaps I can help you," she suggested.

He glanced at her soberly.

"Can you bring me light?" he asked. "I have a thousand men who are wounded. Five hundred of them cannot live unless they are cared for quickly." He rose with a sigh and paced the floor. "And what do I have? Only one little bit of a candle to see by! How can I work with that?"

Clara took him by the arm and led him to the open door. "Look at the barn," she said quietly. "Isn't it well lighted?"

Dr. Dunn stared at the barn in surprise. It

was indeed well lighted. And here and there in the field outside, the golden light of lanterns danced above the corn.

"Where did you get those lanterns, Miss Barton?" the doctor asked, amazed.

"I brought them with me, Dr. Dunn. It's my business, isn't it, to assemble supplies?"

"Have you any to spare?" he asked.

"All you can use, I think," she answered. "There are four boxes left."

"God bless you," he said gratefully.

Clara walked back to the barn and sent the lanterns to the house. Soon it was aglow with light. Dr. Dunn was saving many lives.

Meanwhile, Clara had missed Reddy.

"Where has Reddy gone?" she asked the workers. "I haven't seen him for an hour."

No one seemed to know. Clara went to the barn door and looked out into the night. There was a lull in the fighting now. Only an occasional shell was bursting on the battlefield.

"Reddy!" called Clara. "Are you working in the barnyard?"

There was no answer, but suddenly she saw two men carrying a stretcher toward the house.

When they saw her standing in the stream of light at the open door, they turned toward her.

"Miss Barton!" one called. "Please come over here."

She went to them quickly. "Who is it?" she asked.

"It's Reddy, Miss Barton, the brave little water boy."

"Reddy!" gasped Clara Barton. "What has happened? Let me help him!"

One of the stretcher-bearers spoke gravely.

"He's beyond your help, Miss Barton. Reddy is dead."

Clara stared at the thin boy's figure covered by a plain white sheet. She did not lift the sheet from his face. She wanted to remember Reddy as the brave, excited boy he had been that morning when he had driven the mule team, crying: "Giddap, mules, and make time!"

"How did it happen?" she asked the men.

"He tried to save our flag, Miss Barton," they told her. "It was left in the crevice of a rock on the Union battle line. A Rebel saw him try to take it down—and shot—"

Clara Barton turned away, choking back a

"A Rebel saw him try to take it down—and shot—"

sob. Reddy was dead! Reddy, who was only fifteen years old.

The golden glow of the lanterns lighted Clara Barton's face. She was very tired and her heart was grieving. She had loved the water boy as if he had been a young brother.

Tomorrow she would pack the lanterns and move on to other battlefields. Again there would be shot and shell. Other young boys like Reddy would die.

Clara covered her face with her hands. Lanterns in the field, she thought, to light the way—to death. When would it all end? When would this cruel war be over?

CHAPTER ELEVEN

A Ride in the Storm

TWO years after the Battle of Antietam, the Civil War was still dragging on. Clara Barton went from battlefield to battlefield to keep up the splendid work she had started.

In June, 1864, she was at the front just outside of Petersburg, Virginia. Northern troops were besieging the town with bombardment after bombardment of heavy cannon fire. Clara had set up her station not very far from the battle line where thousands of men had already been wounded or killed in two bloody engagements. Boys as young as Reddy were fighting in the thick of these battles. One of them was Larry Brown.

When Clara Barton found him, he was tossing feverishly on an army cot in a hospital tent. His whole right arm had been shattered by an enemy shell.

Clara bent over him with sympathetic eyes.

"Your arm is badly hurt, Larry," she said very gently. "But I'm told you will get well. Is there anything you want while we are waiting for the surgeon to take care of it for you?"

The boy looked up at her with big brown eyes. It was clear that he did not know her, even though he had once been one of her aides.

"Mother," he murmured.

"Yes, Larry."

Clara spoke tenderly. This was not the first time a sick or wounded boy had mistaken the kindly little figure of Miss Barton for his mother. She bent down close to him to catch the sound of his faint voice.

"Cake," he was murmuring. "Chocolate cake."

He was delirious and thought he was back in his mother's kitchen where he had often eaten his favorite chocolate cake! Clara leaned closer to Larry, hoping he would hear her speak.

"I'll bake you a cake," she promised. "A

big chocolate cake—the best you ever tasted!"

She couldn't be sure whether Larry had heard her or not, because he did not answer. But that night she baked the chocolate cake in the kitchen of the little house which the army had provided for her.

"I am glad I decided to do this now," she thought, as she put the icing on it. "The wind is howling like mad and I can never sleep when there's a storm."

She heard a frightful roll of thunder. It was followed by a flash of lightning which lit up the landscape beyond the kitchen window. Suddenly she was startled. Had she seen a party of horsemen outside in that brilliant flash of light? She strained her eyes to look again. Then she went to the kitchen door.

"I shall have to be careful," she told herself. "They may be Rebels and here for no good." Suddenly she turned and looked at the kitchen clock. "Why, it's almost midnight!"

She opened the door a crack. No, she had not been mistaken. When the lightning flashed again she could see several men on horseback in a clearing behind the house. They were talking among themselves.

One of the men dismounted and started toward the kitchen. In another flash of lightning, Clara could see that he was a soldier and his uniform was blue.

"I hope we didn't frighten you, Miss Barton," he said as she drew him into the warmth of the kitchen. "I am Sergeant Stephens and I've come to tell you that the mine at Petersburg has exploded. The casualties are frightful."

Clara was stunned.

"The Petersburg mine has exploded!" she repeated slowly. "Added to all the battle casualties, this is indeed bad news."

Sergeant Stephens' face was grim.

"It is already rumored," he told her, "that over five hundred of our men were killed. There must be almost two thousand wounded. Over a thousand others missing and—"

"Take me to Petersburg," Clara Barton demanded in a low voice.

The sergeant looked amazed.

"In this frightful storm, Miss Barton?" he asked.

"Storm or no storm," she answered, "I'm going. Please have my horse saddled, Sergeant. Tell the men who are with you to come in out of the rain. Will you ride to Petersburg with me?"

"I shall be honored to take you," said the sergeant.

He left to see that her horse was saddled. The storm was becoming violent and he was worried. Horses are often frightened by thunder and lightning. He hoped they would have no trouble with the animals on their way to Petersburg.

In a few moments Clara came out of the house dressed in a big army coat for her midnight ride.

"Hello, men," she said to the horsemen.

"Hello, Miss Barton," the men answered her in a chorus. They watched the sergeant help her mount her big horse. The animal was nervous. His nostrils were quivering as though he already scented danger.

"You are very brave to ride a skittish horse twenty miles through this storm," one of the men said.

Clara tightened her hands on the reins.

"I have been riding horses since I was five years old!" she said quickly. "This news you have brought is frightful. I must get to Petersburg and do what I can at once."

"She's game clear through," one horseman remarked to another as she and Sergeant Stephens disappeared into the darkness.

The night was pitch black. Clara Barton and the sergeant were only able to see each other when the lightning flashed in crazy streaks of fire. The rain fell in torrents.

Clara Barton could feel her horse quivering. She spoke to him soothingly.

"Steady, boy! Steady! Don't you feel my hand on the reins? I am not frightened, so why should you be?"

But even her gentle words and her firm hands on the reins failed to comfort the horse. Finally he stopped and just stood still, frightened and neighing.

"In trouble, Miss Barton?"

She could not see Sergeant Stephens, but she could hear him above the rumble of thunder. And she knew he was reining his horse in beside hers.

"I'm not in trouble, but my horse is," she answered. "Are you sure I'm not riding a mule? I'm afraid I can't make him budge!"

Sergeant Stephens laughed in spite of this new problem.

"I'm sure you're not riding a mule," he answered. Then he spoke to his own horse and discovered that it, too, refused to go on. "I think we'll have to let these horses rest until they make up their own minds what they want to do," he said.

Never would Clara Barton forget this stormy night. Rain-drenched and cold, she sat huddled in her saddle, waiting for her horse to "make up its mind" to go on to Petersburg. She had never experienced anything like it. If the horses had run away in the storm,

Never would Clara Barton forget this stormy night

she would not have been surprised. But to have them stop dead! And no amount of urging would make them move. There they stood in one spot—just stood—shivering.

"Looks as though we'll have to sit it out, Miss Barton," Sergeant Stephens murmured.

"I'm afraid you're right," Clara said ruefully. She sighed, thinking of the precious time they were losing and of the wounded men who needed her help.

The horses never moved until dawn. Then, with the first streaks of light, the terrible storm subsided. Quickly Clara and the sergeant rode on toward Petersburg.

Clara Barton was tired when she came to the scene of the frightful mine disaster. But she went to work at once to care for the men who had been hurt. Other workers were amazed at her strength. The wildness of wind and weather had had no effect upon her, it seemed. As long as there was a wounded man who could be helped, she simply refused to admit she was tired. She even remembered to send word back to her kitchen to have an aide give Larry Brown the chocolate cake!

One nurse told her that many soldiers at

Petersburg were unaccounted for or missing.

"Someday," murmured Clara, "all the missing men of the army must be found if possible. The government owes it to their families. And when this cruel war ends—"

But the war did not end until almost a year later. And by that time Clara Barton was already busily engaged in a search for missing men. Even before the fighting ceased she had begun to receive letters from the families of men who had disappeared.

"They seem to come from everywhere!" she said to Sally one March morning as they sat together in Clara's room in Washington. "Here's one from a woman whose son disappeared after the battle at Gettysburg. She doesn't know whether he was killed or taken prisoner. And here's another—"

She picked up a letter from the large pile before her.

"This is from a wife whose husband was captured at Fort Donelson. She's never heard from him since then and is afraid that he died in prison. They're all alike, Sally! In every letter someone asks me to find out what has happened to a son, a brother, a husband, or a father. And somehow I must help them, even if I have to use every penny I own to do it."

"It will be a tremendous task," Sally said soberly. "Will the government give you any help?"

"I think so," said Clara. "Yesterday I wrote to President Lincoln, asking him to let me be

a general correspondent for the families of missing men. If he agrees to this, I'll set up an office and get some assistants to help in the search. I feel sure that he will agree."

President Lincoln did agree to Clara Barton's request. Only a few days later he sent out the following notice from the White House:

"To the Friends of Missing Persons: Miss Clara Barton has kindly offered to search for the missing prisoners of war. Please address her at Annapolis, giving her the name, regiment, and company of any missing prisoner.

(Signed) A. Lincoln"

Now Clara Barton began to receive more letters than before. She set up an office in an army tent in Annapolis and hired several clerks to help list the names of thousands of missing men and to write to prisons asking for information about them. One of her assistants was a young man from Switzerland named Jules Golay.

Jules Golay had come to America before the beginning of the war. He had fought with the Union soldiers and had been wounded. Clara had met him in a hospital in Virginia and had written letters for him to his family. He had never ceased to be grateful to her. Now he was glad to be able to help in her search for missing men.

It was a long and difficult search. For four years Clara and her workers were able to find out what had become of thousands of men, but thousands more were still missing. One day Clara discovered that it would take much more money than the government had given her to carry on the search. She had already used a great deal of her own money on it, and there was not much left.

"Oh, what shall I do?" she groaned to Jules Golay. "We can't stop the work now! Little boys are still waiting for their fathers to come home, and little girls are tugging at their mothers' skirts, saying, 'Maybe he will come tomorrow!' We've got to keep faith with them, Jules!" Suddenly she brightened. "I know what I'll do!" she cried.

Young Jules looked at her with admiration.

"What will you do, Miss Barton?" he asked.

"I'll go on a lecture tour!" she answered. "I'll tell people all about our work and why it must go on. If they will pay to hear me speak, we can raise money that way!"

Clara Barton made speeches all over the country, and raised a great deal of money for her cause.

One night she stood on the stage of an opera house in the East. The house was filled with men and women who wanted to hear her tell of her work in hospitals and on the battlefields. With a little smile, she stepped forward, ready to speak.

"Dear friends!" she began. "It is my—"

Suddenly her voice was gone. She tried again to speak, but no words came. She had no voice at all! And suddenly she collapsed on the floor of the stage.

Her voice had gone because she was exhausted with her years of war work and her long search for the missing soldiers. The doctor ordered her to rest for three years. And for that rest, to go to Europe.

CHAPTER TWELVE

Clara Has Visitors

CLARA BARTON had been in Europe more than a year. She had traveled in Scotland, England, and France. Now she was in Switzerland, living in Geneva with the family of Jules Golay. They were happy to have her because she had been kind to Jules. He had written them many letters telling all about his friendship with the "wonderful Miss Barton."

One April afternoon as she walked down the Golays' garden path, she saw a little girl swinging on the gate. The child jumped off and ran to meet her.

"I thought you'd never finish writing your letters!" she exclaimed. "Are we going for our

She saw a little girl swinging on the gate

walk now, Miss Barton? May we stop at the pastry shop and buy some little cakes?"

Clara Barton laughed. "Yes, Carlotta, we'll take a good long walk and on the way home we'll buy lots of little cakes," she said.

She took Carlotta by the hand and started through the gate. But the child pulled back and her blue eyes widened.

"Look, Miss Barton," she said. "Here come a lot of men walking toward us. They all have beards and they're wearing long-tailed coats and high silk hats."

"So they are!" replied Clara, watching the visitors curiously. She knew at once that they were men of importance in the city of Geneva.

They approached her now with great respect. One tall man acted as their spokesman.

"You are Miss Barton, I am sure," he said with a bow and a smile. "The little lady who did such big things in America. My friends and I have come to ask your help in a most important matter. Can you spare a few minutes of your time?"

"Indeed I can," Clara replied. "Carlotta, we'll have our walk later. Won't you come into the garden, gentlemen?"

She led the way into the garden and they all seated themselves under the trees. Then the tall man introduced himself.

"I am Dr. Louis Appia," he said, laying his high silk hat on the grass beside his chair. "These gentlemen and I have come to talk with you about the International Red Cross."

"The Red Cross?" asked Clara. "What is that?"

"It is a society which has been formed to help people who have suffered because of war," Dr. Appia replied. "Let me tell you a little about it."

He crossed one long leg over the other and began.

"Eleven years ago a young Swiss gentleman named Henri Dunant was in Italy during wartime. He was horrified when he saw the wounded on the battlefield and realized how many men died there for lack of care."

"Just as I was horrified on the battlefields at home," said Clara softly.

Dr. Appia nodded and went on with his story.

"Dunant could not forget what he had seen. He decided that an organization should be formed which would care for the wounded of any country wherever a war was being fought."

Clara Barton leaned forward eagerly.

"What a wonderful idea!" she exclaimed. "But how difficult it would be to form such a society!"

"Nevertheless it has been done!" Dr. Appia said with a smile. "Dunant and I, with three other men, formed the society several years ago. We named it the International Red Cross. Then we invited men from many countries to come to Geneva to draw up a set of rules for the society. Those rules are part of a treaty which is called the Treaty of Geneva. Twenty-two countries have already joined the Red Cross and signed the treaty. But the United States will not do so. Can you tell us why?"

"No," said Clara thoughtfully. "I can't." She turned to one of the other gentlemen. "Tell me," she said, "do your Red Cross workers go right onto the battlefields?"

"They do, and they are never fired upon," the man replied.

"Neither are their ambulances nor their supply wagons," said a third gentleman. "All countries who have joined the International Red Cross have agreed to this. They have also agreed to protect all wounded men and those who care for them. Red Cross workers are regarded as neutrals. They are never captured. When their work is finished they are allowed to return safely to their own lines."

"But when men are busy fighting, how can they recognize these workers?" asked Clara Barton. "Do you have some special sign?"

"Indeed we do," said Dr. Appia. "We chose the flag of Switzerland for our symbol, because our society was founded here, and reversed the colors."

He pulled an arm band from his pocket and unfolded it. A bright red cross gleamed on a white background. "This," he said, "is the symbol which protects us—the symbol of the International Red Cross."

"The International Red Cross." Clara Barton repeated the words slowly. "Gentlemen, I think it is a wonderful organization. I cannot understand why the United States has not joined it. Perhaps it is because the people there do not know enough about it. When I get home, I shall tell everyone I meet."

Dr. Appia smiled and rose from his chair. "Then we may hope that you will help us, Miss Barton?" he asked. "You will try to persuade your country to sign the Treaty of Geneva and become a member of the International Red Cross?"

"I shall do my very best," Clara promised, rising to her feet. "Thank you, gentlemen, for coming here. I hope that I shall see you all again."

She shook hands with each of the men. Dr. Appia left her a pamphlet which had been written by Dr. Henri Dunant. It would tell her, he said, about the beginning of the Red Cross and what it hoped to accomplish. Clara promised to read it, as she accompanied the men to the garden gate. When they had departed, she turned back to the house.

Carlotta was waiting for her at the door.

"Are you ready for our walk now, Miss Barton?" she asked eagerly.

Clara tousled her pretty curls. She liked this little girl who was a small cousin of Jules Golay.

"I am sorry, Carlotta, but I'll have to ask you to wait a little longer. I have an important pamphlet to read which my visitors left me. But later on, we will go for sure, and then we'll buy your favorite spice cakes!"

As Clara Barton went to her room, her mind was filled with what she had just learned about the International Red Cross.

"I wish I were feeling better," she thought. "I'd start for home at once, and get to work. I'll rest more, so I'll get back my strength more quickly. Then I'll go home and work night and day until I have persuaded my country to join this wonderful organization."

But even as Clara Barton made these fine plans, trouble was brewing in Europe which would change them. On a warm July day, dreadful news spread throughout the land.

France had declared war on the kingdom of Prussia, which was part of Germany. Soldiers of both countries were marching off to battle.

CHAPTER THIRTEEN

A Bow of Red Ribbon

CLARA BARTON stood in the doorway of a large, airy room at the headquarters of the International Red Cross in the Swiss town of Basle. Scores of women were seated in the room, making dressings for use on the battlefields. Clara watched them for a moment. Then she turned to the young woman who stood beside her.

"What a big, clean place this is!" she exclaimed. "And how many, many workers you have!"

The young Grand Duchess Louise smiled and nodded. Several weeks earlier she had called on Clara and had invited her to visit the Red Cross Headquarters. Now she spoke with pride.

"Every woman here considers it an honor to work for the Red Cross," she said. "They spend many hours here. It is true of countless women in other European countries too. All of them, through the Red Cross, help the soldiers in the field. But come, let me show you our warehouses."

She led Clara Barton through the warehouses and showed her their great store of supplies. For the first time in her life, Clara saw things needed for soldiers, in quantities beyond her dreams.

"You see," said the young duchess, "we all work together." She pointed to different labels on boxes which had not yet been unpacked. "Here are supplies sent to us from Austria—and this big box of blankets just came in from Italy. Over there's another box of surgical supplies sent to us from France."

Suddenly she turned and laid her hand on Clara's arm. "If only you would join us in this work!" she exclaimed. "It is all so new! We have plenty of money and materials but no skilled directors. And I have heard so much about how able you are to start things moving and to get them done!"

Clara was deeply touched. Her doctor in America had told her to rest for three years. Only one of those years had passed. She was still having trouble with her throat and she still grew tired very easily. Yet she could not refuse to help when her help was so sorely needed.

"I will join you," she told the duchess at last. "I will work as hard here as I did at home."

Basle lies close to the borders of France and Germany. Heavy fighting was now going on near the French town of Mulhouse, and Clara Barton decided to go to Mulhouse as quickly as possible. One morning she and another Red Cross worker, a Miss Margot, climbed into a carriage and set out together.

The ride in the carriage to Mulhouse was a most exciting one. Only a mile out from Basle, a sentry stopped them.

"Halt!" he commanded. "Halt at once!"

Miss Margot leaned out of the window.

"We are Red Cross workers," she explained. "My companion is the great American lady, Miss Clara Barton."

The sentry suddenly smiled.

"Pass on," he said respectfully.

Six miles farther up the road they met a crowd of French refugees, hurrying through a driving rain toward Switzerland. There were hundreds of them. Some rode in wagons piled high with household goods. Others drove cows and oxen. A few poor peasants pushed carts filled with chickens and children.

"Look at their faces!" murmured Clara. "Poor souls! They are terrified."

Suddenly there came a cry.

"Turn back! Turn back!" the refugees were shouting at them. "The Prussians are coming! You will be killed!"

But in spite of the shouting, they went on to Mulhouse. They had scarcely reached the Red Cross headquarters in the town when they received a message from Dr. Appia to go on to Strasbourg.

"Strasbourg!" echoed Miss Margot wearily. "In this rain and mud!"

Clara Barton smiled almost gaily.

"It is a challenge, my dear," she said. "Be of good courage and let us get started."

Almost twenty-four hours later, they reached the walls of the ancient city. Here again they ran into trouble. The Germans were getting ready to besiege Strasbourg. The American consul had already hired an omnibus to take Americans out of the city before the bombardment started. But he was overjoyed to see Miss Clara Barton! Both he and the vice-consul were veterans of the Civil War.

"We can't permit you to stay here, on account of the bombardment, Miss Barton," he explained. "But if you and Miss Margot will ride in the bus it will take you to the German outposts near Karlsruhe."

"Good," said Clara, remembering that the Grand Duchess Louise had turned her castle in Karlsruhe into a hospital for soldiers. "We'll take the bus."

An American flag was fastened to the front of the bus, and for a time, the travelers had no trouble in passing picket lines. But when they reached the first German outpost, a sentry stopped them.

"What flag is that?" he asked, pointing to the Stars and Stripes.

"An American flag," Clara Barton replied. "You must let us pass."

"No," said the soldier firmly. "I've been in America—in Mexico—and I've never seen a flag like that. Go back where you came from!"

Clara saw that he was determined not to let them go on. Suddenly she turned to Antoinette Margot.

"Have you a Red Cross badge?" she asked.

The girl looked unhappy. "No—I'm so sorry."

"Never mind," said Clara.

She had always liked red and she had fastened her collar that morning with a bow of red ribbon. Taking it off, she hastily fashioned it into a cross which she pinned to her sleeve. Then she leaned out of the carriage and showed it to the sentry.

"You see this?" she demanded. "We are both nurses!"

The sentry smiled and saluted.

"Excuse me, please," he murmured. "I did not know. Pass on!"

The driver whipped up his horses and the omnibus rolled on. Clara Barton looked down at the red cross on her arm. It was the first time she had ever worn the symbol and it had served her well.

A few days later, she and Miss Margot arrived at Karlsruhe Castle in Germany. The Grand Duchess Louise was delighted to see them. She showed them the Red Cross flag which floated above the castle.

"Even if Karlsruhe is attacked by the French," she told them, "that flag will protect us, for the castle is now being used by the International Red Cross."

Clara Barton worked hard at Karlsruhe Castle and on near-by battlefields. Then she and Miss Margot went back to Strasbourg. The bombardment of the city had lasted one hundred days. Many people were living among the ruins. They had lost everything they owned. Winter was coming and their clothing was in rags.

With her own money Clara bought materials. She opened a workroom and invited women and girls to come there to sew. Each day they were paid for their work, and more than thirty thousand garments were made by their busy hands. They grew to love Clara Barton and she stayed in Strasbourg for almost two years. But at last her thoughts began to turn toward home.

She opened a workroom

"How good it will be," she thought, "to see Sally and David and all the rest of the family again!"

She wanted to go to Italy first and then to the Isle of Wight. And then, perhaps, to London. When she told the duchess about her plans, that lovely lady said:

"It is for you to choose the place where you will be happy. But no matter where you go, our hearts go with you. You have done so much for us in Europe, and have served us all so well that you will always be remembered as one of the greatest women of our time." She laid her hand on Clara's. "And I hope that you will be able to persuade your government to sign the Treaty of Geneva and become a part of the International Red Cross."

Clara Barton's eyes were very bright.

"It will be like a crusade to me," she said softly. "I am going to do my best to found the Red Cross in America."

CHAPTER FOURTEEN

"Such a Long Struggle!"

IT WAS New Year's Day, 1878. Clara Barton was visiting old friends in Washington, D. C. Mr. John Hitz and his wife had invited her to stay with them, now that she was in the city to see high government officials about signing the Treaty of Geneva.

Mrs. Hitz was giving a New Year's Day reception. Clara looked very pretty. She was wearing a green velvet dress in which she had recently stood to have her portrait painted. As she mingled among the guests, she talked with a government printer whose name was John Defrees. He had heard about her interest in the International Red Cross and had decided to help her.

"But what can you do for me?" she asked him softly, smiling.

"I can arrange an interview for you with President Hayes," he said. "Would you like that?"

"Like it!" echoed Clara. "If only I might talk to the President himself about the Treaty of Geneva, why—" Her eyes suddenly sparkled like a gay young girl's. "Why, Mr. Defrees, almost anything could happen!"

He smiled at her enthusiasm.

"I will try to arrange for you to see him on January third. I will take you to the White House myself."

On the date that he had promised, Mr. Defrees called for Clara Barton in his carriage. She was wearing a fur-trimmed bonnet and shawl, and she gripped her purse tightly because it contained a precious letter for the President. It had been written by the president of the International Red Cross at Geneva, and it explained why it was important for the United States to set up an American Society of the Red Cross.

When they reached the White House, Clara Barton was taken to the parlor where the wife of the President was entertaining callers.

Mrs. Hayes rose graciously to greet Clara Barton.

"So you are Miss Clara Barton!" she said with a warm clasp of her hand. "I am proud to meet you. I have heard so much about your splendid work in the Civil War, and how you served in Europe on the Franco-Prussian battlefields."

Clara smiled.

"We must all work, Mrs. Hayes. There is so much to be done in wartime."

The First Lady motioned Clara to a near-by chair and asked a servant to tell her husband that Miss Clara Barton was waiting.

"Now," she said, turning back to Clara. "Tell us something about the organization you call the Red Cross."

Clara Barton's eyes twinkled. "I could talk all day long about the Red Cross!" she exclaimed. And she began to tell the ladies what the Red Cross stood for and how its work was carried on.

"It seems like such a splendid organization," one lady said. "I wonder why our government will not join it."

"I've been given many reasons," Clara Barton replied. "One man told me that the United States does not want to join any organization which has been formed in a foreign country. Another said that we did not need the Red Cross here, because we are not at war."

"Does the International Red Cross help only those who have suffered because of war?" Mrs. Hayes asked.

"Yes," said Clara Barton, leaning forward eagerly. "But there is no reason why it couldn't do more than that. Here in America we don't have as many wars as they do in Europe. But we do have terrible fires and floods and epidemics of sickness where people suffer greatly. I believe that there should be a Red Cross Society in every state, and that it should stand ready to help whenever one of these great disasters occurs."

Mrs. Hayes had started to ask another question when President Hayes entered the room. Clara Barton rose and he shook hands with her cordially.

"Well, Miss Barton," he said, looking down at her, "what can I do for you?"

"I will read the translation," the President said with a smile

"I bring you an important letter, Mr. President," Clara Barton said, taking an envelope from her purse. "Here, Mr. President. It is in French, but there is an English translation with it."

"I will read the translation," the President said with a smile.

He read it through and turned again to Miss Barton. "This letter concerns a treaty, so it must be turned over to the Secretary of State," he told her. "I will have to leave you now, because I have Congressmen waiting for me in my office. But I will give you a note to Secretary Evarts, Miss Barton, so you may explain your case to him."

Clara Barton smiled.

"That is all I require, Mr. President," she said. "And thank you, very much, for talking with me."

Clara Barton left the White House filled with hope that the United States Government would soon sign the Treaty of Geneva. But four days passed and she heard nothing. She wrote to President Hayes, thanking him for seeing her and saying how glad she had been to meet his lovely wife. Then again she waited.

The Secretary of State, it seemed, was not greatly interested in the Red Cross. He was too busy to see Miss Barton and had turned the matter over to Assistant Secretary Seward. Secretary Seward declared firmly that the United States was not interested in the International Red Cross and would not sign the Treaty of Geneva.

"But I am not discouraged," Clara told Mr. Defrees. "And I shall never give up."

"I don't believe you will," he said admiringly. "You're a woman of great determination, Miss Barton."

Week after week, month after month, year after year, Clara Barton worked to make people realize the tremendous value of the Red Cross. She wrote pamphlets about it and had them printed. She talked with Congressmen and important officials in every branch of the government. And suddenly she realized that ten years had passed since she had made her promise to the duchess before sailing for America.

"Ten years—a whole decade!" she said one day to her friend, John Hitz. "And still America refuses to join the International Red

Cross." She sighed. "It's such a long struggle!"

"But you'll keep on trying," he said. "I know you will."

Clara smiled a rueful smile.

"Good things are not easily won," she murmured. "Yes, I'll keep on trying."

CHAPTER FIFTEEN

The Rivers Roar

IT WAS not until Chester Arthur had become the President that Clara Barton's long, hard struggle to establish the Red Cross in America came to an end. She was sitting alone in the parlor of her lovely house in Washington when the news came.

"What is it, Tom?" she asked a servant who entered the room.

"Here's a message for you, Miss Barton." He handed her an envelope.

It had come from the State Department, and Clara tore it open with trembling fingers. In the next moment she knew that her great dream of founding the Red Cross in America had at last come true.

The United States would sign the Treaty of

Geneva and the American Red Cross would be born. Because of her valiant efforts to establish it, Clara Barton was asked to become its first president.

"When this news reaches Europe," John Hitz told her, later that evening, "there will be bonfires on the hills! You will be honored by persons of high rank in many different countries!"

But Clara Barton had little time to think about bonfires or honors. She was soon very busy choosing people to be her fellow workers. A young medical student named Julian Hubbell was among them.

It would be Dr. Hubbell's duty to go to places where disaster had struck. He would either go with Miss Barton or send reports back to her if she could not be there.

Disasters were not long in coming. The Mississippi River floods in midwestern valleys! Famine in Texas! Cyclones! An earthquake in Charleston, South Carolina, and yellow fever in Florida! Then, in 1889, there came the Johnstown Flood.

In the high green mountains of Pennsylvania, a dam above the city of Johnstown had broken. Angry rivers were roaring down the valley. Already four thousand people were dead and twenty thousand were hungry and homeless.

Clara Barton and Dr. Hubbell arrived in Johnstown on the first train able to get through from the East. Together they made their way about the city, wading in mud, climbing around among broken locomotives, broken timbers, and wrecks of houses! They saw railway trains tangled with piles of iron wire. "And as for the people," Dr. Hubbell exclaimed, "I have never seen so many people caught like rats in a trap."

The dirty waters of the Conemaugh River eddied and swirled before them. Bodies of the dead floated aimlessly by. Clara covered her face with her hands to shut out the dreadful sight.

Dr. Hubbell spoke to her in a comforting voice.

"Don't forget that help is coming to Johnstown," he said. "The militia is already here with General Hastings in command. They tell me some food has already arrived from Pittsburgh. Other cities will send help and—"

"And there will be doctors from Philadelphia on the next train that reaches here," Clara said, turning away from the river. "I notified the Red Cross there before we left. Come, we will arrange to have our tents pitched high on the hills, and I'll set up a headquarters at once."

As the rescue work in Johnstown began, help poured in from many places. It was as though the sound of waters that had thundered down upon the helpless town had been heard around the world.

Under Clara Barton's direction, soup kitchens were organized where the homeless people could come for food. Six buildings, later known as "Red Cross Hotels," were put up to shelter the people and furnish them with free supplies. Houses were built by some of the men of Johnstown and furnished by the Red Cross. Meanwhile Clara Barton and her workers fought against disease and guarded against fires. And they took care of frightened children in their tents upon the hills.

There was eleven-year-old Johnny who had lost his whole family in the flood. Clara allowed him to sleep on a cot in her tent because he had seemed so forlorn. Early one morning, he awakened her, crying:

"Miss Barton, do you hear singing?"

She sat up on her bed and listened. Could it be possible? Was it really a young girl's voice?

"Jesus, lover of my soul,
Let me to your bosom fly,
While the nearer waters roll,
While the tempest still is high."

She and Johnny were not dreaming. A girl was singing, but her voice was tremulous with fear. Hurriedly, Clara Barton dressed and rushed out of the tent.

"Call Dr. Hubbell and the field workers, Johnny!" she cried. "I have a feeling we'll need them!"

She ran quickly down a hill to a deep ravine where flood waters were still flowing. Wreckage lay piled along the muddy shore, but in the middle of the stream the current was very swift. Clara shaded her eyes from the early morning sun.

"Look, Johnny! Oh, look!" She pointed to a strange sight.

"Look, Johnny! Oh, look!"

"It's a little girl on a raft and she's tied to a post!" exclaimed Johnny.

The girl, adrift on the swiftly moving waters, was being borne nearer to where they stood. Johnny cupped his hands to his mouth and called to her in a strong voice:

"Hello, out there! Help is coming!"

Meanwhile two field workers reached the spot. The two men launched a small boat into the churning waters. In another moment they were poling their way out to the middle of the stream where the girl on the raft was a helpless prisoner.

Clara Barton breathed a sigh of relief when she saw them reach the raft. As it bobbed about in the muddy water, one of them managed to climb aboard. He untied the rope which bound the girl and soon they were heading for shore.

Clara Barton opened her arms when at last her workers brought the girl to her. The child seemed to be about twelve years old. Her gingham dress was soaking wet. Her long red-gold curls were matted with rain, and her blue eyes were filled with terror.

"You are not to be frightened now," Clara

Barton said, as the girl dashed falling tears away. "What is your name?"

"Becky," the child answered. "My father tied me to the raft so's I wouldn't get swept away, but now my whole family's drowned. I thought if I'd keep singing, help would surely come."

Clara's kindly arms tightened around her.

"It is a wonderful thing, Becky," she said, "to keep on singing in the face of disaster. Come with me now, child. The Red Cross will take care of you."

CHAPTER SIXTEEN

Flags Above the Stairs

CLARA BARTON was standing in the parlor of the Red Cross House in Johnstown. Gathered around her were people whom she had helped during the first dark days of the flood. She had worked with them for five long, hard months.

Now they no longer needed her. She was leaving to go back to her home in Washington. And many grateful men, women, and children had come to say good-by.

She was talking to a minister of one of the churches in the town when Becky tugged shyly at her skirt. The white-haired minister looked down at the child and smiled.

"You're Becky, aren't you?" he asked. "I think you're the little girl who was rescued from the raft. Someone pointed you out to me as you came into the building."

"Yes, sir, I'm Becky," the girl answered soberly.

Clara Barton laid her hand on Becky's pretty hair.

"She has been a great help to us," she said affectionately. "I think she has carried more messages for me than any child in Johnstown!" She smiled at Becky, who held out a newspaper.

"Your name's in this, Miss Barton," Becky said. "And everyone is talking about the wonderful things it says about you."

"Really?" laughed Clara. Then she turned again to the minister.

"I have a copy of the article, too," he said. "It is from the *Johnstown Daily Tribune.*" He took a newspaper clipping from his pocket. "Let me read it to you, Miss Barton."

"Oh, no, sir!" Clara Barton's face flushed. She did not like to be praised before such a large crowd. But the minister smiled and began to read what had been printed in the paper. People in near-by groups paused in their talk to listen.

" 'Men are brothers, yes, and sisters, too, if Miss Barton pleases,' " read the minister. " 'The first to come, the last to go, she has indeed been an elder sister to us, nursing, soothing, tending, caring for the stricken ones through this season of distress such as no other people ever knew—such as, God grant, no other people may ever know. Picture the sunlight or starlight, then try to say good-by to Miss Barton.' "

There was silence in the room as the tall, white-haired man finished reading this tribute. But a moment later there was a burst of loud applause. Then a spokesman for the people stepped forward and presented Clara with a gold pin and locket set with diamonds and an amethyst. Tears gathered in her eyes.

"It is so beautiful," she said. "I shall keep it always and the people of Johnstown will always be close to my heart."

Now they gathered closer to bid her an affectionate good-by. When her train left the station that afternoon, they and many others stood and waved to her. She could see Becky and Johnny in the crowd, both of them in tears because she was leaving.

Clara Barton had many problems to meet when she arrived in Washington. And as the years passed there were other disasters in other parts of the country and in foreign lands. When these occurred, Clara Barton and her Red Cross workers went wherever they were needed.

Meanwhile, she had built a new home in Glen Echo, Maryland. It was eight miles from Capitol Hill, just outside the District of Columbia, on the historic Potomac River.

The house was a large one because she had planned it to be a sort of central warehouse for Red Cross supplies as well as a home. It was also to be a meeting place for her friends. Dr. Hubbell and other staff workers often remained there with her for weeks.

"Your house is shaped like a steamboat, Clara!" Dr. Hubbell teased one day. "But I must admit it's comfortable and you've made every room look pretty."

She looked at him and smiled.

"I like it because it has so many windows. And chimneys and turrets and towers," she added. "It is really hard to know where it begins and ends!"

"You're right," said Dr. Hubbell. "It's a most adventurous house!"

Cheerful fires glowed in the rooms in winter, and in summer, sunlight made them bright. A wide hall ran through from the front to the rear of the house with living rooms on either side of it. The Red Cross office was at the western end of the hall. The library and bedrooms were on the second floor.

Every room in the house had the red cross on its walls or furniture. There were gifts that had been given to Clara by humble people of various countries as well as the great ones. And there were trophies, books, souvenirs, and paintings she had gathered in her travels. The main hall and the principal rooms were hung with gaily colored flags from many countries.

"This house shows," said Dr. Hubbell, "how much you have traveled and how people love you."

"I love Glen Echo," Clara exclaimed. "I can look across the river into the mountains of Virginia where I marched with soldiers in the Civil War. And every room brings back many memories."

Although she was now, as years go, quite an old lady, Clara Barton seemed ever young. She was small and slender. Her voice was soft, her eyes were bright, and she loved pretty clothes! She often wore a dress with a long silken train which gave her the regal air of a queen.

One morning in May she sat in her office at Glen Echo talking with Dr. Hubbell about a book she was writing. He was still her most important field agent and her best friend.

She looked at him, smiling.

"You look like a warrior this morning, Julian. All you need is a coat of armor to resemble King Arthur of the Round Table!"

"I am not handsome like King Arthur," Dr. Hubbell laughed. "And all I have is a pen instead of a sword." Suddenly he sighed. "I ought to have a hundred pens, Clara. Our Red Cross correspondence has become so huge."

"I, too, should have a hundred pens!" Clara exclaimed. "There is so much to say in this Red Cross book I'm writing." She glanced down at the notes and papers scattered on the desk in front of her. "I hope it will lead everyone in the world to love the Red Cross."

"What are you going to call your book?" asked Dr. Hubbell.

" 'A Story of the Red Cross.' And I hope it will be an inspiration to young and old everywhere."

"I'm sure it will be," said Dr. Hubbell. "And I don't like to interrupt you, but I think that I shall have to this morning."

"Important visitors coming?" asked Clara.

Dr. Hubbell smiled.

"A group of boys from a school in Cleveland are being brought here by their teacher. A Mr. James Reid, I think."

"Children are always important," said Clara as he paused.

"Like thousands of other people, they want to see Glen Echo," Dr. Hubbell went on. "But they want, even more, to see you. They have heard as much about the Angel of the Battlefields, Miss Clara Barton, as they have about General Grant or General Lee! I hope you'll have a moment to give them."

Clara fingered the china inkwell on her desk.

"I'll have more than a moment," she said quickly. "The Red Cross will need the help of all the boys and girls of America."

Dr. Hubbell rose from his chair.

"I'll let you know when they arrive," he said. "Meanwhile, I'll leave you to your writing."

When Dr. Hubbell had gone, Clara Barton picked up her pen. Before beginning to write, she glanced out of the wide window. As she looked at the blue mountains beyond the river, she remembered the Civil War.

"If only the Red Cross had been organized then as it is now!" she thought wistfully. "Better care could have been given to our soldiers, and thousands who died might have lived!"

Just then she saw a horse in the field close

by. This horse was Clara's special pet and she called him Baba. He was a war horse and sometimes she fancied that he must remember the sound of bugles blowing just as she did.

"When the boys come, I must show them Baba," she thought. "They would surely love to see a war horse!"

When the boys arrived, Dr. Hubbell showed them many treasures in the Glen Echo house. Few other persons, he told them, had achieved so high a goal as had courageous Clara Barton. He read them a fine poem which she had written, called, "The Women Who Went to the Fields."

"But when shall we see her?" one boy asked impatiently as they returned to the wide hall.

Just then Clara Barton appeared at the head of the stairs. The sun was slanting through a stained-glass window. It made the flags above her radiant with color.

The boys were surprised because she was so tiny, and yet she walked like a royal princess. They moved back a bit bashfully into one group as she approached them. Then they saw her smile.

Then they saw her smile

"Hello, boys!" she said merrily. "I'm so glad you have come. Does Glen Echo please you?"

"Yes. Oh, yes!" they cried in chorus.

"Then come with me," she invited them. "I want to show you my war horse, Baba. He is my favorite horse, and has learned to answer to a bugle call like the best of soldiers!"

She stood for a moment, waiting, while they prepared to follow her. Above her, on the wall, hung a lovely portrait. Below it was an inscription in gold:

CLARA BARTON

FOUNDER OF THE AMERICAN RED CROSS

About the Author

Olive Price was born in Pittsburgh, Pennsylvania. There she went to school and college, and later took her first job—as advertising copywriter in one of Pittsburgh's largest stores. After her first trip to New York, at eighteen, she published her first book of plays. Since then, she has written over a hundred plays. In 1948, she began writing books for young people, too, and has been busy at it ever since. She likes dogs, and has a shepherd-collie for company while she is working. She also likes to poke around odd New York shops—mostly bookshops—and to explore country roads in her car.

About the Artist

Ruth Ives was born in Canada, but her family went to live in California when she was only six. Even then she showed a talent for drawing. When the time came, she went to the Chouinard School of Art in Los Angeles for three years, and won a scholarship. Then she went to New York. It was her lifelong ambition to illustrate children's books, but for eight years she did advertising art and illustrations for such magazines as *Good Housekeeping, House Beautiful,* and *Mademoiselle.* Then she married and went back to California. She lives there now with her husband, two children, and a pair of Siamese cats. Her daughter, who is eleven, and her son, who is eight, are both thrilled that their mother at last is doing what she has always wanted to do—illustrate children's books.

Signature Books

"Names That Made History"

ENID LAMONTE MEADOWCROFT, *Supervising Editor*

THE STORY OF LOUISA MAY ALCOTT
By Joan Howard. *Illustrated by Flora Smith*
THE STORY OF JOHN J. AUDUBON
By Joan Howard. *Illustrated by Federico Castellon*
THE STORY OF CLARA BARTON
By Olive Price. *Illustrated by Ruth Ives*
THE STORY OF DAN BEARD
By Robert N. Webb. *Illustrated by Everett Raymond Kinstler*
THE STORY OF BEETHOVEN
By Helen L. Kaufmann. *Illustrated by Fritz Kredel*
THE STORY OF GOOD QUEEN BESS
By Alida Sims Malkus. *Illustrated by Douglas Gorsline*
THE STORY OF BUFFALO BILL
By Edmund Collier. *Illustrated by Nicholas Eggenhofer*
THE STORY OF DANIEL BOONE
By William O. Steele. *Illustrated by Warren Baumgartner*
THE STORY OF KIT CARSON
By Edmund Collier. *Illustrated by Nicholas Eggenhofer*
THE STORY OF GEORGE WASHINGTON CARVER
By Arna Bontemps. *Illustrated by Harper Johnson*
THE STORY OF EDITH CAVELL
By Iris Vinton. *Illustrated by Gerald McCann*
THE STORY OF WINSTON CHURCHILL
By Alida Sims Malkus. *Illustrated by Herman B. Vestal*
THE STORY OF CHRISTOPHER COLUMBUS
By Nina Brown Baker. *Illustrated by David Hendrickson*
THE STORY OF CRAZY HORSE
By Enid LaMonte Meadowcroft. *Illustrated by William Reusswig*
THE STORY OF DAVY CROCKETT
By Enid LaMonte Meadowcroft. *Illustrated by C. B. Falls*
THE STORY OF MADAME CURIE
By Alice Thorne. *Illustrated by Federico Castellon*
THE STORY OF GENERAL CUSTER
By Margaret Leighton. *Illustrated by Nicholas Eggenhofer*
THE STORY OF AMELIA EARHART
By Adele de Leeuw. *Illustrated by Harry Beckhoff*
THE STORY OF THOMAS ALVA EDISON
By Enid LaMonte Meadowcroft. *Illustrated by Harve Stein*
THE STORY OF DWIGHT D. EISENHOWER
By Arthur J. Beckhard. *Illustrated by Charles Geer*
THE STORY OF LEIF ERICSON
By William O. Steele. *Illustrated by Pranas Lapé*
THE STORY OF STEPHEN FOSTER
By Esther M. Douty. *Illustrated by Jo Polseno*
THE STORY OF BENJAMIN FRANKLIN
By Enid LaMonte Meadowcroft. *Illustrated by Edward A. Wilson*
THE STORY OF GERONIMO
By Jim Kjelgaard. *Illustrated by Charles Banks Wilson*
THE STORY OF ULYSSES S. GRANT
By Jeannette Covert Nolan. *Illustrated by Lynd Ward*

★1 *Born in Oxford, Massachusetts, December 25, 1821*

★2 *Begins her first day as a schoolteacher, 1836*

★3 *Receives a pass through the lines to distribute supplies and nurse wounded Civil War soldiers, 1862*

★4 *Establishes an office to locate soldiers missing in action, 1865*

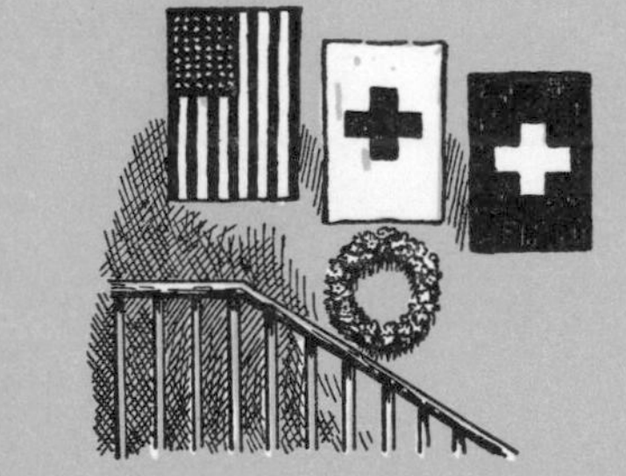

★10 *Dies at Glen Echo, Maryland, April 12, 1912*

★9 *Works to relieve suffering caused by the hurricane at Galveston, Texas, 190*

GREAT EVENTS
IN THE LIFE OF
CLARA BARTON
Helps organize military hospitals
ring the Franco-Prussian War, 1870
6
Supervises the distribution
of relief to the poor
in Strasbourg, Germany, 1871
Brings Red Cross aid to the victims of the
Johnstown, Pa., flood, 1889
7
Becomes the first president
of the American Red Cross, 1881